what's new in
SCIENCE

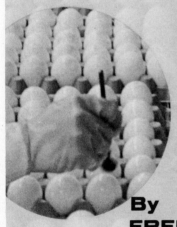

By
FRED REINFELD

STERLING PUBLISHING CO., Inc. New York
MAYFLOWER London

SCIENCE BOOKS BY FRED REINFELD

MIRACLE DRUGS and the NEW AGE of MEDICINE

RAYS—VISIBLE and INVISIBLE

TREASURES of the EARTH

URANIUM and OTHER MIRACLE METALS

Second Printing, February, 1961

40972
Mar. '61

© Copyright 1960 by Fred Reinfeld
Published by Printed Arts Co., Inc., New York 16, N.Y.
Distributed by Sterling Publishing Co., Inc.
419 Fourth Avenue, New York 16, N.Y.
Manufactured in the United States of America
Library of Congress Catalog Card No.: 59-12986

Contents

Enzyme "X" . . . Diagnosing a drop of blood . . . Stapling blood vessels . . . Dacron blood vessels . . . A potent hormone . . . Artificial kidneys . . . New blood for old. VACCINES, CHEMOTHERAPY AND ANTIBIOTICS—Vaccines . . . A vaccine for measles . . . Vaccine cocktails . . . Fooling the viruses . . . The conquest of tuberculosis . . . Chemotherapy, or the quest for new drugs . . . A new pain-killer . . . Curbing the Staphylococcus . . . Cure for hookworm and roundworm . . . Tranquilizers to overcome shock . . . Shrinking brain tissues . . . A drug to remove cataracts . . . Asthma relief . . . Reserpine specialized . . . The search for new antibiotics . . . New form of penicillin . . . Overcoming penicillin allergies . . . An antibiotic from the liver . . . An antibiotic from bacteria . . . Medicated bird feed. GENETICS. OTHER MEDICAL DEVELOPMENTS—How the brain acts as a tape recorder . . . Electrical charges in the brain . . . Electronic artificial nerve cells . . . A sleep machine . . . Pills for the deaf . . . The juvenile hormone . . . Radio waves for medical treatment . . . Virus of trachoma discovered . . . Safeguarding the food supply . . . A new surgical mask . . . Mending broken bones . . . The "mechanical cow"

A CAR THAT DOES NOT TOUCH THE GROUND: Curtiss-Wright's Air-Car is one of a group of air-cushioned vehicles that travel just off the ground. Though it is powered by a conventional gas engine, it uses neither wheels nor transmission (see page 49).

Electronics

It is literally true that not a day passes without the discovery of some new electronic device or some improvement in existing electronic products. In 1940 the electronics industry, with sales of 1 billion dollars, was 49th in the list of American industries. By 1958 it had reached 5th place, with sales of over 13 billion dollars. And no end to this expansion is in sight.

Electronics has been defined very simply as "anything that uses electrons." The first great advances in this field came with the invention of the vacuum tube and the improvements in it that made long-distance telephony and commercial radio broadcasting possible.

The next great advances were based on research during World War II, which gave us radar and electronic computers. The isolated knowledge that high-frequency signals bounced off solid surfaces led in the 1930's to a rudimentary method of detecting approaching aircraft. As radar systems underwent intensive improvement and refinement during the feverish days of World War II, they eventually became so complex in reporting speed, height and direction of aircraft that an electronic brain had to be supplied to them. Thus the electronic computer came into existence.

Computers have now become commonplace, and they are being endowed with powers and capabilities that as little as ten years ago would have smacked of the wildest vagaries of science fiction. Radar has been harnessed to a variety of vitally important uses, such as guiding planes and ships and charting the projected course of hurricanes.

Wartime research also contributed to the rapid development of television, which is destined to have a great many applications aside from the most obvious one—commercial telecasting.

The General Electric Company, for example, developed a television camera tube which is so sensitive to light that it can "see" far beyond the levels of human vision. It was this tube, installed in a special camera manufactured by the Bendix Aviation Corporation, that made it possible for the submarine "Skate" to navigate under the ice packs of the polar region and probe the dark side of the ice, while submerged, to detect the spots where it was possible to surface safely. General Electric scientists are now adapting this tube for such uses as viewing dark railroad switching yards, subways and major highways.

Another notable trend, miniaturization, started with the appearance of the transistor. This has innumerable uses, ranging from missiles to tiny radios. Micro-modules, described later on, have continued the miniaturizing trend.

Beyond any doubt we are on the threshold of revolutionary changes based on new applications of electronics. For example, John L. Burns, president of the Radio Corporation of America, sees the classroom of the future in these terms:

"Tape machines will run prerecorded lessons especially geared to the level of the students, ranging from the slow learners to those who are highly advanced. Each pupil will follow the lesson with headphones. Whenever he has a question, he will be able to talk to the teacher directly on his intercom without disturbing the rest of the class . . . Lining the sides of this classroom will be soundproofed, air-conditioned private study booths for individual recitation and research . . . If the classroom teacher wants to refer to a library book, he will consult his 'television directory,' and dial a number. Instantly a microfilm edition of the book will appear on the television screen."

RCA Executive Vice President E. W. Engstrom foresees the day when a one-inch electronic cube will be able to choose one code signal out of a million as part of a world-wide communications system, so that "each person may be called no matter where he or she is—on land, sea, in the air or even in outer space."

Compact electronics

In 1948 the Bell Telephone Laboratories introduced "a tiny device that serves nearly all the functions of a conventional vacuum tube." This device was the transistor, which uses less power than a vacuum tube, is more resistant to temperature extremes, and is

8

A RADIO ON A TEASPOON: A micro-module receiver, equal to a six-transistor radio but smaller than a lump of sugar, fits on a teaspoon with room to spare. This equipment can perform all circuit functions. Geared for space-age uses, micro-modules scale down electronics equipment to one-tenth normal size. In some cases the reduction is even more startling.

hardier in the event of severe shocks. The transistor also has the advantage of requiring no warm-up period. Whereas a vacuum tube operates by heating a metal filament, the transistor is a crystalline substance such as germanium or silicon which starts working as soon as an electric current is passed through it.

The transistor ushered in the age of electronics miniaturization. This tiny device made it possible to reduce the size of missiles to manageable proportions. Use of the transistor, together with printed circuits, resulted in miniature radios and other hi-fi instruments. They have many other applications, in airplane beacons, air-conditioning units and burglar alarms, for example. A soldier can carry a radio set in his helmet; a civilian can easily conceal a hearing aid.

More recently there was a further revolution in miniaturizing when the United States Signal Corps and RCA introduced the micro-module. This is a tiny ceramic block, about 3/10ths of an inch square, that contains electronic components. With 27 of these fitting into a cubic inch, they act as oscillators, amplifiers and all the other elements of an electronic circuit. They can be powered from a conventional electricity source or by button-sized batteries.

The use of micro-modules has made it possible to reduce some military electronic devices to a twentieth of their former size. A working radio no larger than a fountain pen has been successfully demonstrated, and wristwatch radios no larger than a sugar cube will be available in the not too distant future. Micro-modules will also lead to the introduction of pocket-size record players and dictation machines.

Miniaturization has gone even beyond the micro-module in General Electric's "tunnel diode," a tiny device which is less than one-fourth the length of an ordinary paper clip. The diode works a hundred times faster than a transistor, is unaffected by powerful radiation and comfortably withstands temperatures of −452 degrees Fahrenheit. Anticipated uses for the tunnel diode include: radios smaller than any known at present; midget electronic computers; amazingly small electronic circuits for guided missiles.

A revolutionary vacuum tube

The tremendous advances made in the electronics field have all depended on the familiar cathode-ray tube which produces electrons in a high vacuum after it has heated up. Valuable as this vacuum tube has proved to be, it has several drawbacks: it does not start functioning until it has warmed up sufficiently; and sooner or later the filament burns out, so that the tube has to be replaced.

After several years of research at the Army Signal Research and Development Laboratory at Fort Monmouth, New Jersey, Dietrich Dobischek invented a new kind of tube which is free from these drawbacks. This tube requires no heat and goes on almost instantane-

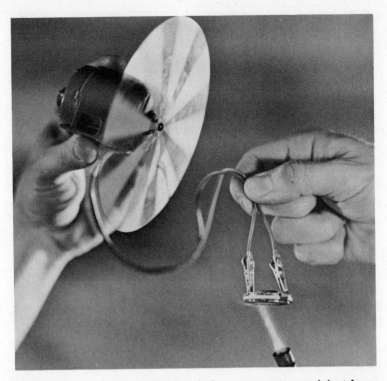

LITTLE GIANT: A tiny vacuum-type thermionic converter gets enough heat from a blowtorch to power a motor that causes a pinwheel to rotate. Further research is expected to triple the converter's power output.

ously when power is supplied. The new tube is so durable that it can outlast the other components of a radio or television set.

The heart of the new tube is a series of thin, porous layers of magnesium oxide deposited on nickel and treated at high temperature in oxygen. Then, once a positive charge has been imparted to the coating, the tube is ready to operate.

Converting heat into electricity

General Electric scientists have developed a "thermionic converter" that directly converts heat into electricity. In its present state, the device turns 9 per cent of its heat energy into electricity, but further improvements should eventually step up its efficiency to 30 per cent, putting it within respectable reach of the efficiency rating of turbogenerators, the conventional form of producing electricity.

The thermionic converter is made up of two tungsten plates placed a very slight distance apart. This space is filled with a vapor in a near-vacuum state. The cathode plate is heated to about 1,500 degrees Centigrade; the anode plate to about 1,000 degrees Centigrade. The cathode is hot enough to release electrons, while the anode is not. The difference in temperature causes a flow of electricity which is powerful enough to light a small bulb.

The Westinghouse Electric Corporation has developed another thermoelectric cell for the Air Research and Development Command. Called the "TAP-100" (terrestrial auxiliary power, 100 watts), it produces enough electricity "to light brightly an average room, operate a one-eighth horsepower electric motor or power the average portable TV set."

The device is the size of a medicine ball and weighs 40 pounds. Westinghouse claims that its thermoelectric cell can "transfer into a comparatively large-scale device the advantages of thermoelectric power generation previously attained only in smaller units." The prototype generator operated on propane gas, but is capable of working with other fuels as well.

While these results may not seem impressive, there are enormous potentialities in thermoelectricity. There is the possibility, for example, of using the sun's heat to produce electricity and of using solar energy to power spaceships.

The Russians have made considerable progress in meeting small power requirements by using thermoelectric cells. Radio transmitters with a limited broadcasting radius are powered by thermoelectric cells heated by a kerosene stove. Russian electronics experts are experimenting with thermoelectric units for heating and also for refrigeration. In all they have over 30 uses for thermoelectric cells, particularly in areas that lack conventional sources of power.

An electric fuel cell

For many years scientists have been trying to develop an electricity-producing fuel cell that would be small, compact and independent of any outside power source, such as engines, furnaces, boilers and turbogenerators. Francis T. Bacon, working in a laboratory at

Cambridge, England, has demonstrated a fuel cell that is eminently practical. (Several American research workers, including General Electric scientists, have developed similar devices.)

Bacon's fuel cell, which he calls the Hydrox, is a gas-charged battery that produces electricity from a chemical reaction. The device is made up of a series of porous nickel plates separated by a liquid—potassium hydroxide (caustic potash) which acts as the electrolyte. The cylinder of plates in the first demonstration model is about 30 inches long, with a diameter of 12 inches.

Oxygen and hydrogen are fed into the partitions around the individual cells at a pressure of 400 pounds a square inch at a temperature of about 390 degrees Fahrenheit. The contact between the nickel and the oxygen ionizes (electrically charges) the atomic particles, which then unite with the hydrogen. The chemical reaction causes a flow of electric current with a power output of about 5 kilowatts.

The fuel cell's generating efficiency is remarkably high—65 per cent, as compared to 30-40 per cent efficiency for the best power stations working with conventional fuels.

The control gear of the fuel cell is large enough to fill a truck. But it is capable of operating an assembly a hundred times the size of the demonstration model. In another two years it should be possible to build a cell with an output of 500 kilowatts, enough to move a railroad car at economical cost.

Many other possible uses are already foreseen, in view of the undeniable advantages the fuel cell offers. It is noiseless and does not generate excessive heat.

In contrast to atomic energy, it involves no problem of dangerous waste products. As it has no moving parts, it is easy to maintain. It readily withstands vibration and is unusually resistant to extremes of climate.

The one great drawback of the fuel cell is that it produces direct current, which in many cases has to be converted to alternating current.

One of the earliest uses of the fuel cell will probably be in space satellites. Scientists also anticipate that it can be adapted for use in submarines and surface vessels. Somewhat later it may come into use for supplying power for trains, earth-moving equipment and industrial handling devices. Because of the comparatively small space the cell and its controlling gear take up, it will be an ideal form of standby power equipment to be used in case of power failure.

Another likely development is a gradual reduction in the size of the control gear to perhaps one-tenth of its present size. This would make it practical to install the fuel cell in automobiles and buses.

Several other types of fuel cells are in various stages of development. The Carbox, an invention of H. H. Chambers, has also reached the practical stage. This one works on a combination of oxygen and carbon-containing matter, such as kerosene. Another fuel cell operates at atmospheric pressure on almost any combustible gas instead of pure oxygen; but it has the drawback of requiring high temperatures—about 1000 degrees Fahrenheit.

Electronic highways

From time to time we hear of methods of electronically controlling the progress of cars along highways. One such plan, described in 1958 by Leslie Flory, supervisor of the RCA General Research Laboratory, would even make drivers superfluous.

No matter what the shape of the road, a continuous cable under each lane can keep cars centered in their respective lanes. This is accomplished by signals that direct an electronic steering mechanism in each car. To control speed, high-frequency circuits in loops are embedded in the roadway; these are attached to electronic computers that register each car's speed and its distance from the car immediately in front of it. This results in another set of signals that either accelerate the car or slow it down to avoid collisions.

Cost is the factor that prevents the installation of such a system. The electronic adaptation of a new car would cost about $200. But the highway installation would be prohibitively expensive: $50,000 per lane-mile. So, until costs can be reduced considerably, such plans for electronic control must be deferred to the distant future. Another method of automation on the highways is discussed on page 44.

Electronics for medical treatment

In the United States the use of electronic devices for medicine has now become so widespread that over $200,000,000 of equipment is sold each year. This includes X-ray machines, electrocardiographs and diathermy units.

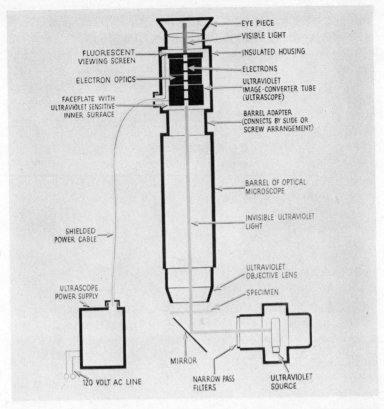

EYE PIECE
VISIBLE LIGHT
INSULATED HOUSING
FLUORESCENT VIEWING SCREEN
ELECTRONS
ELECTRON OPTICS
ULTRAVIOLET IMAGE-CONVERTER TUBE (ULTRASCOPE)
FACEPLATE WITH ULTRAVIOLET SENSITIVE INNER SURFACE
BARREL ADAPTER (CONNECTS BY SLIDE OR SCREW ARRANGEMENT)
BARREL OF OPTICAL MICROSCOPE
INVISIBLE ULTRAVIOLET LIGHT
SHIELDED POWER CABLE
ULTRAVIOLET OBJECTIVE LENS
ULTRASCOPE POWER SUPPLY
SPECIMEN
MIRROR
120 VOLT AC LINE
NARROW PASS FILTERS
ULTRAVIOLET SOURCE

A LOOK AT THE INVISIBLE: The ultrascope converts ultraviolet waves into light waves, making it possible to see objects ordinarily too faint or too small to be viewed with conventional equipment.

One of the outstanding new developments is the ultrascope, a product of the RCA laboratories. This is an electronic tube that can be attached to a microscope. The ultrascope converts ultraviolet images (invisible to the human eye) into visible pictures that can be interpreted by medical researchers. Images too small to be focused by light waves and therefore beyond the power of conventional microscopes, will now become visible as the ultrascope converts ultraviolet waves into light waves.

Another device developed in RCA's laboratories is the sanguinometer, which counts blood cells and other microscopic particles.

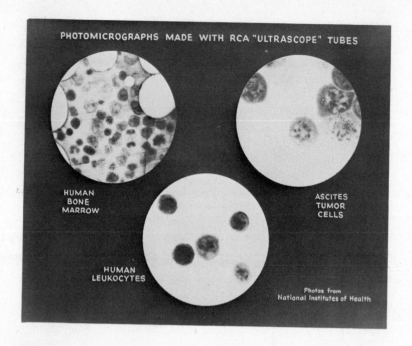

PHOTOMICROGRAPHS MADE WITH RCA "ULTRASCOPE" TUBES

HUMAN BONE MARROW

ASCITES TUMOR CELLS

HUMAN LEUKOCYTES

Photos from
National Institutes of Health

The radio pill, a product of joint research by RCA, the Rockefeller Institute and the New York Veterans' Administration Hospital, is a transistorized frequency-modulation transmitter $1\frac{1}{2}$ inches long and 2/5 of an inch in diameter. Enclosed in a plastic shell for swallowing, it transmits pressure changes in the stomach and intestines. Use of this device should speed up diagnoses of digestive disorders, ulcers and other common ailments.

Closed-circuit color television sets for use in hospital operating rooms are being sold in substantial numbers. Such a machine is of great value in teaching surgical techniques.

Electronic readers for the blind

At a conference of the National Academy of Sciences, research workers from the Battelle Memorial Institute of Columbus, Ohio, demonstrated a new electronic reader that promises to enable blind people to "read" printed and typewritten material.

At its present stage of development, the device translates letters into patterns of musical tones similar to the chords produced by an electronic organ. Eventually the scientists hope to translate the letters into synthesized speech. In its present state, the electronic reader enables trained users to take in from 15 to 30 words a minute.

The electronic reader looks like a portable radio. Weighing nine pounds, it has knobs for volume and light intensity and an electric power switch. There are three basic parts—a probe that moves over the printed matter; a chassis containing transistorized oscillators and an amplifier; and earphones.

The probe is made up of two tiny lights and a lens that projects an image of the printed letter upon a row of "electric eyes" (photocells). Each of these photocells, when it "sees" the black of a printed letter, activates an oscillator to produce a sound with a pitch proportionate to the black part of the letter which is "seen."

An automatic pilot

The first equipment for automatically controlling the flight of aircraft was designed as early as 1912. Since then there have been many improvements in this kind of equipment, which keeps a plane on a preset flight plan and even compensates for variations in flight conditions.

Until very recently it was necessary to redesign this automatic-control equipment for each new type of plane. In 1959 the United States Army Signal Research and Development Laboratories at Fort Monmouth, New Jersey, and the Sperry Phoenix Company of Phoenix, Arizona, announced their success with a new control system that can be used for any type of Army aircraft—airplane, helicopter or pilotless drone.

By using electronic "building blocks" that can be arranged in varying combinations, designers will no longer need to resort to individual tailoring for each kind of plane. The savings in production costs, maintenance and logistics are expected to run into millions of dollars.

Guided missiles

A guided missile is a streamlined tube with a pointed nose cone and narrow wings. It has electric eyes to seek out its target, and an electric brain to follow instructions and make necessary calculations. The nose cone is filled with explosives. Propelled by a rocket or jet engine, such a missile can travel faster than 10,000 miles per hour.

PREPARING FOR COUNTDOWN: (Above)
The transporter brings the giant
"bird" to the launching site.

The missile (a Corporal) is
then lowered onto the
launcher. (Above) Maintenance men ascend the
"cherrypicker," a flexible
platform that enables them
to make adjustments from
any desired position. (Left)
Six seconds after firing, the
missile is gathering speed,
trailed by a pillar of vivid
yellow flame.

There are four ways of guiding a missile. These may be used singly or in combined form:

Beam rider guidance. The missile follows a radar beam directed against an enemy plane. The electronic brain inside the missile keeps it on the radar beam.

Preset guidance. This is used for very long flights to a distant target. The path of the missile toward the target is predetermined before launching. An automatic pilot steers the missile on its way.

Command guidance. A human pilot on the ground transmits electronic instructions to steer the missile. Ground radar aids the pilot to keep the missile trained on the target, while an electronic computer provides the data for his commands.

Homing guidance. The missile detects the target by means of an electric eye (radar or photocells or magnetic detectors).

There are strong indications that missiles will eventually replace most if not all bombers. Missiles are much more accurate, and cheaper in terms of cost and personnel.

There is a great deal of specialization in missiles. Air missiles include air-to-air missiles, which fighter planes may use instead of machine guns against enemy aircraft. It is possible to guide such missiles by electronic commands, or they can be propelled by radar. Air-to-ground or air-to-ship missiles can be dropped like bombs, after which they find their way to the target. After an air-to-ship missile hits the water it discards its wings and in effect becomes a torpedo.

Ground missiles include ground-to-ground missiles such as the intercontinental missiles which can travel thousands of miles after being launched from the ground on one continent to strike a target on another continent. Ground-to-ship missiles are intended for defense against naval attack on a coastal area. It is possible to aim ground-to-air (antiaircraft) missiles at planes that are hundreds of miles away. Such a missile travels faster than antiaircraft fire but can only be effective when it is capable of moving much more rapidly than the enemy planes.

There are also naval missiles. Ship-to-shore missiles can be launched from surface vessels or submarines. Using ship-to-ship missiles, two fleets could carry out a duel while hundreds of miles apart. A vessel can also launch ship-to-air missiles to protect itself against enemy aircraft.

Operated by remote control, missiles can take the place of drones and simulate all the standard maneuvers of a plane while being used for target practice.

In World War II the Germans caused great havoc with their missiles. The V-2 model was 46 feet long, travelled 360 miles per hour, carried a ton of explosives, and contained 30,000 parts, including an automatic pilot. The later missiles have a much greater speed and more complex structure, and carry a nuclear warhead. The only defense against these missiles seems to be to devise an anti-missile that would put the electronic equipment of the invading missiles out of commission (see page 113).

Sperry Gyroscope scientists have made an important contribution by developing a switch that can turn current on or off in 20 billionths of a second. This is less than the time that light, moving at the rate of 186,000 miles per second, takes to travel an inch.

The electronic computers which have the job of calculating the course and speed of an incoming missile and the required course for an intercepting anti-missile were previously not fast enough for the task. The new switch will become a major component in new computers. Since it works about a hundred times more rapidly than switches previously in use, the work of correlating hundreds of radar reports should now proceed much faster.

ELECTRONIC COMPUTERS

A computer is a machine run by mechanical or electronic means to perform mathematical work and to store and select information that has been fed into it. Such a device can do an enormous amount of complicated work in a phenomenally short time.

A large computer, for example, can add or subtract 9000 times a second, multiply 1000 times a second, divide 500 times a second. Mathematicians have estimated that in making arithmetical calculations, human beings average one mistake per 200 digits. For computers the percentage of error in transferring numbers is about one in a billion billion digits.

Electronic circuits work a thousand times more rapidly than nerve cells in the human brain. A problem that might take the human brain two years to solve can be solved by a computer in one minute. Larger computers run to $750,000 and more in price.

A "SMALL" COMPUTER: This portable, economically arranged computer is easy to operate. The electric typewriter handles input and output. The control console contains switches and enables the operator to check on the various operations. Basic electronic equipment is in the closed cabinet.

The heart of the electronic computer lies in its vacuum tubes or transistors. To work properly, a computer must be given instructions; this is called "programing." Computers can be designed for specialized purposes, such as preparing payrolls, guiding airplane flights, running an oil refinery, directing traffic—even playing chess.

Insurance companies use computers to keep a record of every policyholder's account and bill him at the right time. Some banks handle depositors' accounts in the same way. Magazine subscriptions lend themselves to this kind of treatment. Large companies use computers for data-processing jobs such as keeping track of inventories. In oil refineries, in chemical plants and in many factories, computers play an essential role in automation processes.

The military importance of computers keeps increasing all the time. For example, the vast network of continental radar warning systems that covers the United States and Canada is linked together by an elaborate computer setup. Computers keep track of every plane crossing these countries.

Many types of scientific work have been enormously speeded up through the use of computers to carry through calculations that would otherwise have taken years to complete. A spectacular example of this is the development of the H-bomb, which was designed much more rapidly than originally anticipated, thanks to a specially adapted computer.

Computers have made weather prediction more accurate by assembling complex data relating to temperature, humidity, air pressure, winds and rainfall. Government agencies that use a great many statistical analyses—such as the Census Bureau—or a huge accounting system with many individual references—the Veterans Administration, for example—find computers invaluable time- and labor-savers.

There are two kinds of computers: digital, which are slower but more exact; and analog, which are faster but less accurate.

Digital computers, which are the kind that have wider application, count numbers. ("Digit" means a symbol for a number.) They can be used in any process that involves counting or what is known as "logical analysis"—separating into strict compartments (such as sorting, sifting, comparing, matching information). All that is required is to feed the appropriate instructions—translated into mathematical terms—into the machine.

Analog computers are specialized for handling a particular problem. Speedometers, thermometers, loud-speaker volume controls are examples of mechanical analog computers. The reading on these "computers" shows the degree or quantity of the variable that is being measured.

For arithmetical and logical operations, a digital computer has three basic elements: (1) the equivalent of a desk calculator—except that the computer works much more rapidly; (2) a control unit, which determines the order of the processes needed to solve a given problem or perform a given task; (3) a memory or storage unit that preserves the required instructions and keeps a file of all needed numbers and of quantities that have already been calculated in earlier steps and will be needed in a later phase. Reels of magnetic tape, or a cathode-ray tube (very similar to a television picture tube) are among the materials used in memory units.

The tape is magnetized to represent combinations of 1 and 0. By storing the information on a magnetic drum which revolves thousands of times a second, it is possible to get required information very quickly. When the information is obtained, it goes to the output unit and appears on magnetic tape or punched cards.

The operator is seated at a control panel called a "console." If anything goes wrong, a light will flash on to pinpoint the area involved. However, to a certain degree computers are able to find their mistakes and even, in some cases, to correct them.

A digital computer is made up of thousands of electrical circuits that can be switched on and off. In this way the operation of a computer resembles the workings of the nerve cells in the brain.

The computer uses binary arithmetic, which calls for only two digits: one and zero. Then, using the "on-off" principle, circuits that are on represent 1, while circuits that are off represent 0. By combining circuits that are on and off, the computer can give the operator any desired combination of numbers that represent quantities, letters or symbols—depending on the nature of the prearranged code.

A computer works by means of a "program"—a series of instructions fed into it, along with any fixed values that are part of the material that is to be calculated.

First the instructions go into the input section. The computer stores the program in its memory unit. After the computer has made the required calculations, it conveys them to the output section. As necessary, the computer will refer from time to time to the memory unit for instructions, or for the results of preliminary calculations previously executed.

Improvements in computers

Scientists at the laboratories of the National Cash Register Company have developed a remarkable glass rod with a magnetic coating. This rod is about the size of a pin and has a diameter of 15 thousandths of an inch.

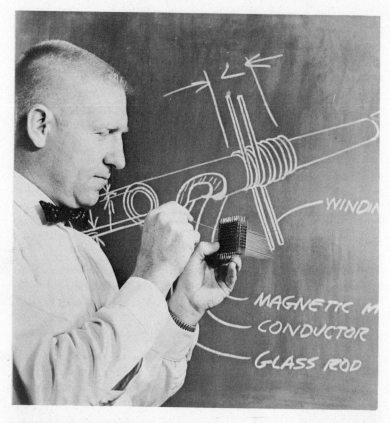

A TRIUMPH OF MINIATURIZATION: Donal A. Meier, inventor of the magnetized glass rod, demonstrates the use of these rods in the memory unit of a computer.

For all its tiny size, this rod represents an important advance in the functioning of digital computers. With a switching time of 250 millionths of a second, it can speed up a computer's "thinking" as much as 20 times.

The tiny size of the rod also yields notable advantages; a rod memory system no larger than a cigarette package can store 8000 bits of information.

The rod is expected to make it possible to navigate missiles and satellites with smaller power sources, thereby increasing their fuel capacity and consequently their range. In addition, the rod functions reliably at temperatures 300 degrees Fahrenheit higher than conventional components. As missiles and space vehicles operate at very high temperatures, this improvement offers promise of more reliable navigation.

The thousands of vacuum tubes used in a computer generate an enormous amount of heat which may cause mechanical difficulties and even breakdowns. Autonetics, a division of North American Aviation Inc., has designed an all-transistorized digital computer which uses no vacuum tubes. This avoids mechanical troubles and also results in a compact machine weighing less than 200 pounds.

The fields in which this computer has proved its usefulness include aircraft and missile design, civil engineering, mechanical engineering, electrical engineering and other scientific applications.

MINIATURIZED TELEVISION: The girl is holding the camera and main control equipment of a nine-pound battery-powered television system designed for use in missiles and space vehicles. The transmitter and camera power supply are on the table in front of her. Image at left, produced by another miniaturized television system, shows remarkably fine definition.

PREVIEW OF THE FUTURE: The Automatically Programmed Tools System perfected at Massachusetts Institute of Technology is operated by instructions from an electronic computer.

At the laboratories of the National Cash Register Company scientists are working on a chemical memory system which would be far superior to the present electronic systems. When perfected, the chemical system will make it possible to store a million pieces of information (such as codes, symbols, definitions, prescriptions, and formulas) on a square inch of paper. The complete Bible could be set up on three sheets of paper.

Automatically directed tools

One of the most critical problems in aircraft and missile production is the manufacture of parts that are highly complex and have to be

COMPLEX BUT PERFECT: These beautifully finished parts look as if they had been turned out by a master craftsman who lavished many hours of work on them.

AUTOMATIC CONTROL: Computer programing operates more rapidly and more accurately than the old methods, simplifying design problems and reducing working time.

produced individually. The perfecting of the Automatically Programmed Tools System (APT) at Massachusetts Institute of Technology has now overcome this difficulty.

APT uses a digital computer to prepare all the information to control the operation of automatically functioning tools that make a part in accordance with specifications. The design information is fed into the input system of the computer, which makes all the necessary calculations and gives the appropriate directions to the tool system.

All the instructions are limited to a vocabulary of 107 basic English words. Each letter has a corresponding number, and the position of holes punched on cards is keyed to a specific number. The computer, supplied with directions in this manner, in turn controls an automatically guided machine tool.

Generally this tool is a high-precision standard machine which is made automatic by adding sensing and control circuits to it. The tool is thus equipped to "read" the numerical instructions and convert them into machine-tool language. The mechanism which does this is known as the "director."

Characteristically, an instruction will be made up of two numbers. One number corresponds to a controlled axis of motion in the machine tool; the other number indicates the amount of time the process will consume. On receiving such instructions, the director operates the machine-tool cutter by causing it to move from one point to another in a specified manner along a directed path in a given interval of time.

A typical instruction might read: "ON KUL, ON SPN, GO RGT, TL LFT, CIRCLE/CTR AT, +2, +3, RADIUS, +5." This means: Turn on coolant, turn on spindle, go right with tool on left side along circle whose center is at $x = +2$, $y = +3$, with a radius of $+5$.

The whole operation may be extremely complex, but it is broken up into a sequence of tasks which are individually quite simple. In this way it even becomes possible to execute quite complicated curves or surfaces in three dimensions.

When the preparation of the directions ("programing") was done by human calculation, the work was very slow, tedious and not always reliable. But computers are taking over more and more of the programing task, performing it with much greater speed and reliability than any human brain could. Much of the subroutine programing is now stored electronically, forming a library reservoir in the computer's memory section. The result is that production becomes more efficient by becoming more automatic. Engineering design problems are greatly simplified; operating time and total costs are greatly reduced.

A world of robots

As electrical machines become endowed with more and more abilities, there is a growing feeling that the process might result in a race of lifeless machines with superhuman brains. Such machines would have the power of making duplicates of themselves.

In 1958 a group of scientists at the University of Michigan Research Institution submitted a report on the parallelism between human and mechanical nervous systems to the Office of Naval Research. The report points out that while the electronic computers can calculate a million or more times faster than a human being. it has always been thought that the machines were dependent on human beings for programing. Such a machine could do nothing original.

But scientists are gradually becoming accustomed to the idea of building machines that can think, learn and perpetuate themselves. Much of this distant prospect was discerned by the late Dr. John von Neumann, one of the greatest mathematicians of modern times.

While a great deal of this thinking is necessarily speculative, there are arresting passages in the Michigan Research Institution's report:

"Logical theory can take into account a special sort of growth, the construction by a machine of a duplicate of itself. It is possible to describe a machine which would perform work useful to humans and then proceed to make an image of itself with the instructions to do useful work. This offspring would, in turn, make an image of itself.

"Even if this is acceptable on the level of mathematics and logic, it is difficult to visualize physical entities that might embody this process. However, as Dr. von Neumann suggested, one might be able to visualize the parent machine paddling about in a sort of thick soup of spare parts.

"The machine scoops up a part at random, tests it to see if it is the one it needs next, and if so fits it into place in the copy it is making of itself. As it completes the copy the parent machine would insert a duplicate of its own instructions and then detach the new machine to begin its working life and then to forage for itself among the available spare parts to construct a copy of itself."

Machines that can learn

Ordinary computers can remember only the data fed into them on punch cards or magnetic tape. Scientists are therefore trying to design machines that will be capable of learning from experience and assimilating what they learn into their electronic circuits.

Dr. Frank Rosenblatt, research psychologist at the Cornell Aeronautical Laboratory of Buffalo, New York, has designed a machine he calls the Perceptron for the United States Navy. This machine is said to be the first non-living mechanism able to "perceive, recognize and identify its surroundings without human training or control." Though Perceptron will make mistakes at first, Dr. Rosenblatt anticipates that "it will grow wiser as it gains experience."

The first model, built at a cost of $100,000, will have about a thousand electronic "association cells." These will receive electric impulses from a scanning device with 400 photocells. This equipment will do the work done by 10 billion cells in the human brain, including 100,000 connections with the eye.

In fully developed form, the Perceptron will remember patterns *it has perceived itself*. This is what makes it startlingly different from ordinary computers which can only remember the information that has been fed into them.

Perceptron uses a camera-eye lens to scan objects or survey situations. Its system of electrical impulses, modelled on the brain's communication system, interprets the data which has been scanned.

Later machines embodying the same principles are expected to be able to recognize people and call out their names. They will be able to read printed and written matter and give speech commands. Eventually they may reach the point of hearing speech in one language and instantly translating it into another language, either in speech or writing.

At University College in London, scientists are building a similar machine which will be able to scan letters of the alphabet and simple words and will then "say" through a loud-speaker what it has seen. It will operate through an electronic network of 4000 tubes. These will be electro-mechanical equivalents of the neurons—the nerve cells of the brain and body.

This requires an analog computer—one that simulates the basic activity of another machine or process. Dr. Wilfred W. Taylor, who designed the machine, gives this example of the computer's learning powers: the machine will easily recognize and spell out the letter "O." However, it will at first have difficulty in distinguishing between "O" and the somewhat similarly shaped "Q." But since the "Q" will bring more electronic circuits into operation, repeated use of these additional circuits will enable the machine to "learn" to distinguish between the two letters.

The designers have placed electric counters in the equipment to indicate how long it takes the computer to "make up its mind." The counter will also measure the electronic strength that goes into its "convictions."

A computer that sees

Step by step, computers are being endowed with the powers of human beings. In one of the most interesting of these projects, scientists of the United States National Bureau of Standards are teaching a computer to "see." The computer is called SEAC (Standards Electronic Automatic Computer).

The scientists installed a photoelectric cell in the machine and

ATOMIC DETECTION: This formidable equipment uses a powerful microscope, television camera and electronic computer to scan and count the paths made by invisible atomic particles in a photographic emulsion.

added a device to enable it to scan a photograph, break it down into 30,000 light and dark squares, and store the pattern in its memory compartment. Whenever the picture is needed, it can be recalled from the memory unit and shown on an oscilloscope as a unit made up of 30,000 light or dark squares.

However, the scientists want to endow SEAC with more than visual memory. Since the machine can recognize printed letters and numbers, it should be possible to go a step further and equip it to recognize diagrams, chemical formulas and more complicated material.

Eventually the computer will be able to do much more difficult work, such as deriving contour maps from aerial reconnaissance photographs, or picking out a specific picture from a rogues' gallery. The advantages of using the computer will be accuracy, speed and absence of the fatigue factor.

How to make mistakes

Electronic computers "think" for human beings. But Dr. Herbert A. Simon of Carnegie Institute of Technology and Allen Newell of the Rand Corporation have set up a digital computer that thinks *like* human beings.

To accomplish this requires novel programing to simulate the process, errors and all, by which human beings solve problems. This is possible because the computer can work with symbols as well as numbers. In fact, the machine can read symbols, move them, store them or erase them, and even compare them.

To follow such instructions as, "Put this symbol at the end of that list," is a simple task for the computer. In time, the designers feel, it will be possible to direct a computer "to print the processes used at each step of the problem-solving process: the methods, what is being noticed and attended to, what plans are formed, what sub-problems are created."

Machines that can reason and learn

Mathematicians and engineers are cooperating in an attempt to design machines capable of drawing lessons from experience and adapting to circumstances as they arise.

There are many kinds of problems, in the spheres of biology, strategy and economics for example, for which classical mathematics can offer no solution. Experienced managers can of course make decisions or form plans that deal with uncertainties. But the contemplated machines, which may take years to build, will perform these functions more effectively.

Some of these problems are on a large scale, an instance being the proper strategy for the United States Air Force. Other problems are more specific—working out the most effective design for an electronic computer, or designing an "autopilot." (This is a computer that can help a pilot find the best way to handle unexpected difficulties.)

A totally different problem is devising a decision-making process for setting up a small business in strongly competitive situations. Proper mathematical "programing" is the element needed to make the machine supply useful solutions. For in that event, automatic-control devices would "learn" as they operate, acting on information from past experience and adapting it to new conditions. Perplexing as the problem is and expensive as the machines are bound to be, they would be comparatively economical because they would improve on the judgment of fallible human beings.

The designing of thinking machines embodies an amusing paradox, for the scientists are stretching human ingenuity to the utmost in order to invent machines which will be the equal, if not the superior, of the human brain.

An international conference on "The Mechanization of Thought Processes" which took place at the National Physical Laboratory of Great Britain brought forth some interesting ideas. In an address to the conference, Dr. Marvin L. Minsky stated that "we can often find simple machines which exhibit performances that would be called intelligent if done by a man. We are, understandably, very reluctant to confer this dignity on an evidently simple machine."

An English delegate, Dr. S. Gill, held out the prospect of a mechanical surgeon which will make incisions with the aid of television "eyes" and stitch up the cuts while at the same time automatically keeping track of the patient's blood pressure, respiration and all other relevant factors.

Another English delegate thought the day would come when most administrative work would be done by machines, eliminating all clerks and most junior executives as well. However, he conceded that human beings would have to remain in the highest executive positions.

A French delegate expressed the belief that machines could revolutionize the practice of law by going through innumerable law tomes to sift out the statutes and precedents applying to each case, and then arriving at a decision after evaluating this material. However, he felt that human judges would still be needed—if only to temper justice with mercy.

A machine that reads

A large corporation which deals with a great many people and has to keep records of each transaction finds that the labor cost of maintaining its records can become prohibitively large. This difficulty arises, for example, in the case of magazines with millions of subscribers and public utility companies whose customers form a huge segment of the population.

To solve this problem, inventors are devising data-processing machines that more than pay for their cost by economizing on payroll. Some of these electronic brains are highly specialized; one machine is able to answer an instantaneous "Yes" or "No" to 128,000 possible questions, many of them requiring intricate calculation.

One of the most interesting data-processing machines is an "Analyzing Reader" known as the "Scandex." This machine replaces innumerable clerks through its ability to read words prepared on a standard typewriter. After scanning the material, the machine disposes of it electronically, either storing it, translating it, or if need be transmitting it by a process similar to teletyping. In punching holes in cards for sorting and classifying, Scandex handles over 100 cards a minute.

One large corporation puts all its dividend checks through a Scandex machine as soon as they have been printed. As the machine scans each check, it punches the amount of the check and the stockholder's certificate number on the face of the check. Then, after the checks are sent out, cashed and returned, they are quickly sorted automatically.

Scandex lends itself to many other types of business transactions. A bank uses it for reading travellers' checks. A magazine processes subscriptions with the machine. A large corporation with 240 sales offices has the sales reports entered by Scandex. Oil companies use the machine for processing the hundreds of millions of invoices that originate through the use of credit cards. The savings realized by the elimination of manual labor run into vast sums.

Computers for research

American industrial and scientific research is turning out an enormous volume of work. Add to this the work being done in other countries, and it is clear that no man or group of men can possibly keep abreast of these achievements. In some cases, it is so difficult and costly to search for relevant information in a scientific field that the work already done has to be done all over again. In fact, it has been estimated that a mere 1 per cent saving in lost and duplicated research time could save American industry 20 million dollars annually.

Throughout the world there are now some 50,000 periodicals devoted to the natural and physical sciences. Some organizations make indices and abstracts of at least the most important articles, but the task is becoming more and more hopeless. The United States Patent Office, faced with a similar problem, is four years behind in processing applications for patents (see page 39).

The Center for Documentation and Communications Research at Western Reserve University in Cleveland points the way to the only practical solution. This is the storing of scientific information in an electronic computer—the Western Reserve Searching Selector. Human operators prepare encoded abstracts of scientific articles and feed the material into the machine, which in turn can supply bibliographies of existing material in typewritten form. The present machine works with vacuum tubes, but soon it will be replaced by a transistorized model that will work 5000 times more rapidly.

The material punched on cards is coded in such a way that the machine supplies information not only on the specific subject wanted, but also on the broad grouping of which that subject is a part. This pioneering attempt at building up a huge but convenient research center is expected to be copied widely.

Air-traffic control

Twenty-six air-traffic control centers are installing electric brains (Remington Rand Univacs) to coordinate information on flight plans, plane speeds, landing details and changing weather data.

Until the computers are put in operation, an airline pilot gets directions from a control center during the course of the flight. He sends in reports which are entered on a flight-posting board at the control center. For each plane handled in this manner the controller stacks rectangular strips on the board. These strips contain the flight-plan information pertaining to each plane.

On each strip there must appear an identification number, the type of plane, its speed, expected time of arrival, altitude and the complete route being flown. In compiling this material and filling it in on the strips, the controllers become so bogged down in paper work that it is difficult for them to give all their attention to the really important work in hand—tracking the flights and giving the pilots new instructions when these are required by changing conditions.

The computers will take over the work of preparing all needed information and assembling it on the strips. This will free the controllers for their main job and help make air travel safer and more efficient.

Blind navigation

The remarkable under-surface voyages of the American sub-marines "Nautilus," "Skate" and "Seawolf" were all made possible by two electronic devices which are both dependent on computer techniques.

Nuclear submarines can remain submerged for 60 days and perhaps more. Having two means of ascertaining their exact location without surfacing, nuclear submarines have acquired great destructive powers (see page 158).

One of the locating systems is known as SINS (Ship's Inertial Navigational System). This device records every motion of a ship and automatically computes the exact distance the vessel covers.

The basic instrument used is an accelerometer. This contains a weight which is left free to move back and forth against springs. The movements of the weight are really a measure of the vessel's acceleration. An electronic computer uses this information to calculate the ship's velocity.

Actually two accelerometers are used—one for north-south motion and one for east-west motion. The accelerometers are held steady in the required directions by stabilizing gyroscopes. The combined action of the two accelerometers, in addition to determining the distance travelled, also gives latitude and longitude readings.

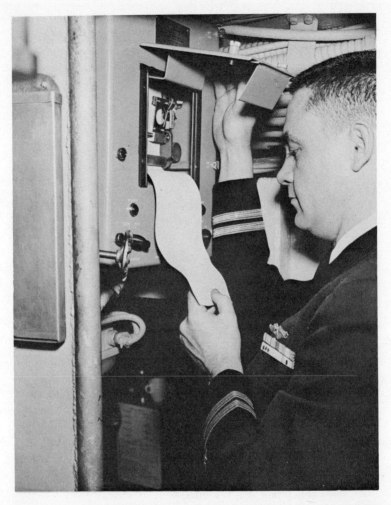

ABOARD THE "NAUTILUS": An officer inspects the revolutionary Submarine Celestial Altitude Recorder (SCAR) which enables navigators to take accurate readings of the location of celestial bodies while the vessel remains submerged. The invention of this device has been ranked in importance with the development of the snorkel.

The other location system is called SCAR (Submarine Celestial Altitude Recorder). Much of the details of its operation are classified, but this much is known: the device, fitted into the periscope, makes it possible to sight the sun, moon or a star without surfacing. The operator presses a switch, and the computer automatically supplies the altitude of the sighted celestial body in degrees and minutes as well as the time in hours, minutes and seconds. The information appears instantaneously on a slip of paper which looks like the bill used at the check-out counter in a supermarket.

The navigation officer then sights one or more additional stars in the same way. By consulting a Navy almanac and preparing a chart to show the intersection of lines from the observations taken, the officer ascertains the exact location of the vessel. SCAR's margin of error is one second in 24 hours.

A computer simplifies Chinese printing

In China illiteracy has always been a serious problem because the Chinese alphabet is made up of thousands of ideographs (symbolic representations of ideas or objects). A knowledge of English is based on familiarity with an alphabet of 26 letters and a few punctuation marks. A well educated Chinese has to master some 6,000 characters; for a scholar, 20,000 characters is a more likely figure.

Samuel H. Caldwell, Professor of Electrical Engineering at Massachusetts Institute of Technology, applied himself for seven years to developing a method of composing Chinese characters just as rapidly as a linotype operator can compose English text. He calls his machine, a combination of a keyboard and an electronic computer, the "Sinotype."

Instead of turning out lead type, the Sinotype puts the Chinese characters on photographic film. The finished job can then be transferred to the "printed" page by conventional techniques.

The Sinotype operates with "Basic Chinese"—a vocabulary of 2,333 basic characters that are adequate for ordinary communication. If necessary, the machine's vocabulary can be expanded to 6,000 characters. The first step before building the machine was to make a detailed analysis that broke down Chinese writing into 21 basic strokes. The Sinotype keyboard has 21 keys, each one representing a fundamental stroke. The operator punches the keys in the order he would use if he were drawing the characters.

As the operator punches a key, it sends a coded signal to the computer. The computer assembles these and compares the group of

MODERN WIZARD: Named for Merlin (King Arthur's legendary magician), this digital computer adds in 6 millionths of a second and multiplies in 5 thousandths of a second.

signals with the coded descriptions of complete characters. The computer then selects the proper character.

The vocabulary of characters is arranged in 50 columns of 48 rows. The machine picks out the desired character and presents it in an optical viewer to the operator. He then presses a bar, causing the character to be photographed. Continuing the process, he sets up his copy in this manner. Although the procedure sounds cumbersome, it is much quicker than might be supposed.

Unruly English

The United States Patent Office plans to build a computer in which to store references to all earlier patent-seeking ideas. The problem is inordinately difficult because a single word can often have a great many possible meanings. The computer can only work properly if it is fed information made up of words each of which has only one meaning.

Simon Newman, an engineer and a lawyer, is devising a synthetic language which he calls "Ruly English" to distinguish it from the "unruly" language which has so many different shades of meaning. In "Ruly English" a word has only one meaning.

The word "through" illustrates the kind of difficulties Newman is trying to solve. It has at least 13 possible meanings. To avoid this ambiguity, Newman invented a synthetic word, "howby," with the invariable meaning of "mode of proximate cause." Though this sounds complicated, it actually leads to helpful simplicity and clarity, as far as operating a computer is concerned.

An electronic chessplayer

Constructing an electronic chessplayer that can play chess is a problem that has a special fascination for some scientists. At first sight this seems strange, since chess has no practical value. But as Claude Shannon, one of the outstanding authorities in this field, has pointed out:

"Chess is a compact little universe. It is a simplified and abstracted form of what we face in the physical world. It has conflict, logic, goals and rules. If we can puzzle these out, we will have clues for the more important and complex things." Perfecting a chessplaying machine, then, would lead to greater knowledge in more important fields.

While the finer points of chess judgment are still beyond the grasp of a computer, it is already becoming evident that Norbert Wiener was justified in anticipating the development of a digital computer that would play as well as "the vast majority of the human race."

The magnitude of the task becomes clear when we realize that all the information about playing the game of chess has to be fed into the computer in combinations of zero and one, the only two numbers used in the machine. Yet this enables the memory section, for example, to store all necessary information about the position of the pieces on the board, and the changes that take place from move to move. The individual powers of each chessman, as well as the squares which each one can move to or is forbidden to move to, are only a small part of the information that the machine requires. The execution of even the simplest instruction may require 5000 steps; yet this takes the computer a trifling fraction of a second. Intensive research will gradually lead to more detailed programing that will refine the machine's powers of chess reasoning.

Medical computers

Computers are expected to play a big role in the hospital of the future. As population expands, the pressures on the medical profession will increase accordingly. The use of computers can avoid a crisis and actually improve the efficiency of medical services.

One obvious and valuable use for digital computers is the storing and interpreting of the medical knowledge that has been acquired in the last 50 years. No one individual can possibly keep up with these discoveries. Unless computers can make this information available for ready reference, much of it will remain untouched.

All existing knowledge of disease symptoms and treatment could be stored in one computer center. This would enable doctors to feed data on symptoms into a computer and get the needed information on proper diagnosis and treatment. Of course, computers would by no means eliminate the doctor from the picture; they would only reinforce his skill.

World magnetism charted

Every five years the United States Coast and Geodetic Survey issues a world-wide magnetic chart to enable navigators to determine the variation of their compass needles from true north. This chart, based on 150,000 geodetic observations, requires calculations that would take one man a century to perform. The computer needs about four weeks for this work.

The need for the calculations arises from the fact that the observations have been made at different times since 1900. As the magnetic field of the earth shifts every year, the calculations make necessary adjustments for the shift that has taken place since the time of the original observation.

A specialized computer

As the use of electronic computers becomes more widespread, designers will turn to smaller models geared to a specialized function. A pioneering example of such a small device is the pocket computer intended for helicopter pilots.

Every helicopter has a payload capacity based on normal conditions. If these conditions change, the payload may turn out to be top-heavy, causing the helicopter to crash. In order to take account of such conditions as temperature, altitude, humidity, wind, distance and ground speed, helicopter pilots have had to make intricate calculations based on figures in a number of charts.

Using the pocket computer, the pilot need only turn a few dials, getting the required solution in a minute or two. In this way he eliminates time-consuming paper work and greatly increases his chances of a safe, swift trip.

Computers for combat use

Scientists have already found more than 70 military uses for electronic computers. The portable machines, some weighing as little as 85 pounds, can be transported conveniently in trucks and helicopters.

The jobs that the computers can do include the analysis of target locations, the calculation of atom-bomb effects and the solution of the problems involved in moving a division. A divisional staff may need as much as three days to work out all the details of moving such a large body of troops; a computer can do the work in four hours.

Eventually the number of man-hours required for data processing and transmitting should decrease about 80 per cent. Under combat conditions, when time is of the essence, the gain in speed will be invaluable.

The machines used for this work operate in the familiar manner of electronic computers. Mathematicians translate distances, speeds, forces and all other relevant factors of a battle situation into numbers. The numbers are keyed to symbols on punched cards or magnetic tape. This material, together with questions prepared in the same way, is fed into the computer. The machine then sets out the answers on a typewriter or in some other manner.

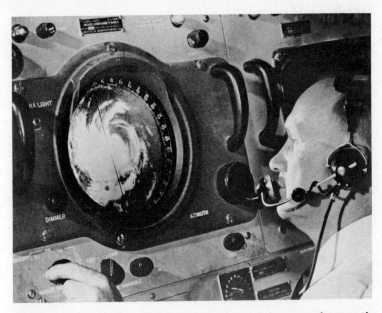

TRACKING DISTANT STORMS: With the aid of this storm-detector radarscope the Weather Bureau operator can follow the course of storms, hurricanes and tornadoes as far as 200 miles away. Note how the image on the screen reveals the circular motion of the swirling hurricane winds.

RADAR

A radar weather "eye"

The New York office of the U.S. Weather Bureau has a radar unit which can spot storms 150 miles away. According to meteorologist Ernest J. Christie, "We can forecast rain or snow down to hours and minutes with the new weather-search unit."

The unit comprises a 72-inch parabolic "dish" inside a plastic dome, two radarscopes in a shack on the roof and a "repeater" radarscope in the Weather Bureau office. "The radar beam sent out by the unit travels until it hits rain, snow or ice crystals, and then bounces back to make milky shadows and shapes on the 'scope. From this picture we can plot the approach of storms." Detecting a storm at a distance of 150 miles provides about six hours of warning notice.

Radar warning system

Narmco Industries of San Diego, California, has developed an improved type of radar antenna that can detect enemy missiles at a distance of 3,000 miles and determine their precise distance, speed and direction.

The new system, known as TETRAC (Tension Truss Antenna Concept), will enable engineers to build radar antennas 20 stories high. Such an antenna will provide greater accuracy of reception and lower construction and maintenance costs than conventional antennas.

The antenna is made of concentric rings of lightweight metal, plastic or glass. The rings hold a giant reflector in place and are stabilized by radial tension rods that function like huge bicycle spokes.

Radar photography

Britain's Royal Air Force has developed a system of radar photography that is capable of supplementing or even replacing visual or photographic reconnaissance. This radar equipment can, for example, identify airfields and measure their runways accurately. It is being improved for installation in the large, speedy V-bombers—the Victors, Valiants and Vulcans.

According to Air Secretary George R. Ward, "We should, under favorable conditions, be able to make an estimate of the number of aircraft assembled on an airfield.

"The Victors would be able to cover an area equal to the whole Mediterranean in a single radar reconnaissance sortie by one aircraft and could give a count of the total number of ships in the area.

"A radar map of an area the size of the United States could be made in one sortie by only four aircraft."

An important possible use of this radar technique would be to carry on aerial inspections as part of a general disarmament agreement.

No-hands driving

According to two scientists of the Westinghouse Electric Corporation, an ingenious radar control system might make it possible to "drive" across the United States with hands off the steering wheel during the whole journey.

The scientists, Dr. Yaohan Chu and P. N. Buford, propose to fit front bumpers with simple radar transmitters and receivers. The cost would be a few hundred dollars. The radar set would detect a thin foil strip or line painted down the center of the road, and steer the car to follow the course of this line.

The guide strip could be coded in dots and dashes, with one pattern, for example, that would cause the car to halt at a stop sign. Another pattern would direct a car—when its radar is set for the purpose—off the road at a major intersection.

The radar scientists believe that theirs is the most practical system that has been offered so far, and they are convinced that it might be in experimental use by 1961 and in general use by 1964. The guidance system could easily be adapted to further refinements, such as an automatic brake that would come into action if the distance between two cars reached a specified limit.

One of the great virtues of this system is that in contrast to other proposals for automatic guidance, it does not require any special mode of construction or any tearing up of highways for installation. It is therefore by far the cheapest of all methods proposed so far.

Ultra-sensitive radar

One of the most remarkable refinements of radar is a new device so sensitive that it can pick out a single enemy soldier at a distance of 6 miles. The new system, developed by the Army Signal Corps and Hazeltine Corporation, can detect a vehicle 12 miles away.

Combat Surveillance Radar, as this device is called, makes use of the Doppler effect to detect slight movements toward or away from the instrument, because such changes produce corresponding changes in the radio-wave frequency reflected from moving objects.

Under combat conditions the radar set is trained in the direction of probable enemy approach. The radar beam covers an angle of 30 degrees. Anything that is moving within this area causes a sound like radio static. The operator, duly alerted, narrows his beam to focus on the suspected object. When the object is properly pinpointed, its characteristic sound will create a revealing pattern on the oscilloscope, giving the operator the information he is seeking.

ELECTRONIC SENTRY: These three photos illustrate operation of the U.S. Army's Combat Surveillance Radar, intended for use in advanced combat areas, particularly where visibility is bad. This portable equipment, utilizing radar with headphones, makes it possible for the operator to detect the movement of enemy groups and vehicles at a distance, even under conditions of darkness or fog.

Padar, not radar

PADAR (Passive Detection and Ranging) is an electronic detection system which may solve the problem of mid-air plane crashes. In a plane equipped with this device the pilot could tell at a glance the exact range, altitude, direction and rate of approach of another aircraft, and immediately maneuver his plane out of danger.

The detection system operates in this way: an approaching plane transmits an electronic signal in a straight line ahead, and another signal to the ground. PADAR picks up the first signal and a trifle later picks up the second signal when it bounces off the ground. The slight time lag enables an electronic computer to determine the range, direction and altitude of the oncoming plane. In this way the pilot is able to avoid a possible collision.

PADAR, developed by the Guided Missiles Division of Fairchild Engine and Airplane Corporation, differs in this respect from radar: whereas radar sends out signals and receives back their echoes, PADAR receives signals transmitted by an approaching plane. Another essential difference is that radar is unable to provide a reading on altitude.

Surface Travel

Air-cushioned vehicles

The principle on which an air-cushioned vehicle operates is a novel one. It is not an airplane as it does not have wings. It is neither ship nor automobile as it travels completely clear of sea or land. Though such a vehicle uses a conventional gas engine, it has no wheels and no transmission. How is the air space formed between the "flying auto" and the land or sea below it? What maintains the air space?

Underneath the car there is an air chamber with a large propeller parallel with the ground. The gasoline engine supplies the power that causes the propeller to whirl. This fills the chamber with air, some of which is forced toward the ground through tiny holes around the edges of the car.

The jets of air that are forced down from the car's rim to the surface have the effect of creating a "wall" that cuts off the escape of the air sucked in by the propeller. As more and more air enters the chamber and remains trapped, there is necessarily less and less space for each molecule of air. With the particles crowding together (becoming "compressed"), their pressure becomes so strong that they lift the car off the ground.

But the compressed air is also the source of locomotion. Once the car is in the "floating" stage, the driver uses a set of rear jets to release some of the compressed air. Working on the same principle as the jet engine of an airplane, this forces the compressed air backward, speeding the car forward.

The air car can do a very effective job on reasonably level surfaces. It can bypass highways and travel across fields or swamps. It is unaffected by poor roads and snow, for these offer no obstacles to it. Similarly, water, desert or ice give the car no trouble. And, since the arc moves through the air it encounters much less friction than a surface vehicle.

A "FLOATING SAUCER": This Hovercraft "flying ship," designed by British engineers, travels 15 inches above the water, using the air-cushion principle. It has been operated with equal success on land. Eventually the designers hope to have a "flying ship" that can travel over 70 miles an hour.

The Ford Motor Company's single-passenger Levacar travels an inch above the ground. Its present maximum speed is 60 miles an hour, and the oil industry, military forces and farmers are expected to be its first users. Curtiss-Wright's Air-Car, which glides along 6 to 12 inches above the ground, weighs 2,500 pounds and can carry up to four passengers.

Engineers predict speeds of up to 500 miles an hour for the most powerful air-cushioned vehicles. They have a tremendous range in size and power—an indication of their great versatility, from family-use cars to transoceanic liners.

However, they still have a great difficulty to overcome—hilly terrain. Whenever such a vehicle tilts at an angle, a certain amount of air necessarily escapes. But sooner or later the designers and engineers will meet this challenge to their ingenuity.

A "flying" ship

British engineers have developed a flying ship that travels on an air-cushion and looks like a flying saucer. It is called a "Hovercraft."

The doughnut-shaped Hovercraft is 30 feet in diameter and weighs 4 tons. Its air cushion is about 15 inches high and less than 2 feet across.

After a successful land-travel test a foot above ground, the craft, built by Saunders-Roe Ltd., had a sensationally satisfactory water test in June 1959 off the southern coast of England.

Christopher Cockerell, the designer of the Hovercraft, hopes to design a "flying" ship for carrying passengers and freight that will be capable of crossing the Atlantic in 36 hours. He believes the best cruising speed would be somewhere between 70 and 100 miles per hour.

A "flying" scooter

A research team at Princeton University's James Forrestal Research Center has developed a "flying" scooter which has a bicycle seat and handlebars on top of its circular base.

As with a bicycle, the rider's body guides the scooter; to turn, the rider leans in the desired direction. A 5-horsepower engine powers the propeller which creates the air-jets that form a 4-inch air cushion. The vehicle's top speed is 15 miles an hour. Its remarkable lifting powers are more than four times those of a helicopter.

Medicine and Mental Health

HEART DISEASE

Although many people are aware that heart disease is the number one killer in the United States, they are less familiar with the enormous amount of brilliant research that is going on in this field. Scientists have discovered drugs that prevent or relieve dangerous conditions; they have devised daring surgical techniques; they are making increasingly diversified use of electronics; they are saving many lives that in former times would have been lost.

Studying heart disease in a tissue culture

The disease that is responsible for more deaths in the United States than any other disease is atherosclerosis. This is the term for a condition of hardening and narrowing of the arteries as fat-like substances accumulate in them. If a blood clot suddenly develops, arteries in this condition are more likely to be blocked than arteries which are large and offer no obstacle to passage of the blood.

Sometimes the clot blocks off one of the arteries that lead to the heart. In this event, a heart attack—lack of nourishing blood moving to the heart—may be the result. If the block is massive or remains for a long time, there may be severe damage to the heart muscle tissue. If a vessel feeding blood to the brain is blocked, a stroke may ensue.

There has been lively argument in medical circles about the role of fatty substances, particularly cholesterol, in leading to these dangerous conditions. But much of the evidence has been inconclusive and subject to dispute. An actual laboratory study of these problems by Harvard University researchers sheds interesting light on these problems.

The investigators grew bits of body tissue in cultures which were nourished with a precisely determined solution. Pieces of human aorta (the major artery that carries blood from the heart) were grown in this way, enabling the scientists to observe the effect of feeding fatty substances to the artery cells.

When a nutritive solution containing 40 per cent blood serum was used, heart and artery cells grew satisfactorily. Later, when cholesterol was added to the nutritive solution, fatty deposits appeared in the artery cells, which became enlarged. If the researchers removed cholesterol from the feeding medium, the cholesterol deposits gradually disappeared from the artery cells, which then resumed their normal size.

Where cells continued to be nourished with the medium containing cholesterol, the fat deposits got larger and eventually the cells died. The researchers also found that if they added saturated fatty acids (rather inactive chemically) to the nutrient medium, the fatty deposits in the cells noticeably increased. If they added unsaturated fatty acids (fairly active chemically), the fatty deposits decreased.

THE HEART CATHETER: This is a long hollow tube which is inserted through an arm vein into the right chambers of the heart. The catheter is a valuable tool for research as well as diagnosis.

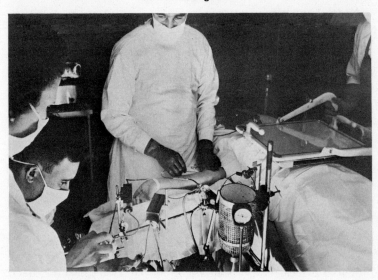

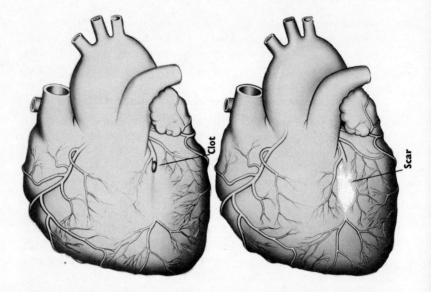

Clot

Scar

HEART DAMAGE: These pictures show the damage caused by coronary heart disease. (Left) Condition of the heart four days after an attack. (Right) After eight weeks: the damaged artery is covered with scar tissue.

These findings are an important point of departure for later, more detailed studies. For example, they show that the atherosclerosis process can go on even in the absence of emotional or physical stress.

And yet there is impressive conflicting evidence. For example, a study by two San Francisco doctors, Ray H. Rosenman and Meyer Friedman, showed that when tax accountants worked their hardest to meet deadlines, the cholesterol content in the blood went up markedly—as did the likelihood of blood clotting.

So here we have a contradictory finding, tending to show that stress rather than diet is the important factor in cholesterol content and blood-clotting time. A third possibility, of course, is that stress may raise the cholesterol level in one person while faulty diet is the cause in another.

Hearts in hi-fi

Even before the invention of the stethoscope, listening to sounds produced by heartbeat was an important part of medical technique.

In recent years, the use of modern sound equipment has greatly extended the range of what can be heard and diagnosed.

Electronic amplifying stethoscopes now give the doctor access to sounds that he could never hear previously. This is made possible by introducing tiny microphones directly into the heart through a long plastic tube. If the heart valves are not functioning properly, or if the blood is flowing turbulently, the appropriate sounds will ordinarily not come through the chest wall. But the amplifying equipment will make them perfectly audible. These sounds can be recorded and played back repeatedly if necessary.

Some authorities expect the use of "intracardiac phonocardiography," as it is called, to become more efficient. "We believe," as one group of experts put it, "that in the future, a multi-purpose catheter can be introduced into the heart to localize very precisely the origin of heart sounds and murmurs."

Moving pictures of the heart

Research scientists of the Picker X-ray Corporation have developed an X-ray unit that enables physicians to examine the workings of the heart on an 8-inch television screen. This ingenious unit also comes equipped with a motion-picture camera which preserves the heart examination for later, repeated study.

Runaway heartbeat

Cardiac arrhythmia (a wild, irregular heartbeat) is one of the most serious complications of many heart attacks. When a blood clot in an artery cuts off the flow of blood to part of the heart muscle, the disorganized heartbeat may develop and cause a lowering of blood pressure. This may deprive the heart of still more blood. The death rate in such cases runs from 60 to 90 per cent.

Dr. Eliot Carday of the University of California Medical School found that prompt injection of the hormone Noradrenalin will step up the blood pressure and bring the heartbeat back to normal, thus saving the patient's life. Administering the drug is a delicate procedure, because an overdose would raise the blood pressure to a point where the runaway heartbeat would recur. The safest way is to administer the drug drop by drop, stopping the treatment as soon as the beat becomes normal.

Preventing brain damage

Temporary heart stoppages are not necessarily fatal, but they may result in serious brain damage because fluid accumulates in brain tissues, with resulting severe injury to the central nervous system. To prevent this, Drs. Jack Zimmerman and Frank Spencer of Johns Hopkins University developed the technique of reducing a patient's temperature to 90-91 degrees and thus slowing down circulation of the blood. This technique is useful in certain types of heart surgery.

The same result can be achieved with the drug fluothane. A research team led by Dr. Robert Orton at Alfred University, Melbourne, Australia, worked out the technique for using fluothane. The drug is an effective anesthetic and is therefore useful in heart surgery cases. In addition, fluothane cuts down the amount of oxygen needed by the body, thus slowing circulation and preventing brain damage.

To avoid the danger of blood clotting, the patient is given an injection of heparin, an anticoagulant. The surgeon can then tie off the main blood vessels and proceed with the operation. An additional virtue of the fluothane technique is that it enables the surgeon to work much more rapidly than is ordinarily the case. The earliest operations with fluothane have been highly successful.

Dissolving blood clots

Fibrinolysin is an enzyme which keeps the coagulating mechanism of the blood on an even keel. Scientists at the Ortho Research Foundation of Raritan, New Jersey, developed a purified form of this human blood fraction which is extremely helpful in treating certain kinds of blood clots.

Previously the development of anticoagulant drugs concentrated on preventing the formation of blood clots. Fibrinolysin (trade name: Actase), on the other hand, dissolves already existing blood clots. It has been used with very satisfactory results on two types of blood clots—those in lung arteries (pulmonary embolisms) and in veins in the extremities (thrombophlebitis).

Much research still remains to be done to determine whether the drug can prove effective in other kinds of blood clotting—for example, coronary thrombosis, a blood clot in the coronary artery of the heart.

Another type of blood-clot dissolver which shows promise when given to victims of a heart attack is called streptokinase, or SK for short. This preparation is made by growing bacteria in large vats in order to obtain an extract that is used to dissolve dead tissues in treating infections.

Dr. Anthony P. Fletcher of Washington University, St. Louis, was in charge of studies on the effect of SK on patients who have had heart attacks.

Early tests with SK have yielded encouraging results with victims of blood clots that shut off the supply of blood to the heart and began to damage heart muscle. If the value of SK is definitely established, there will still remain the problem of preparing it in pure form. At present the process is long and tedious.

Artery grafts

Cerebral strokes are a major cause of death and disability. Dr. Michael de Bakey, of the Baylor University College of Medicine, an internationally known authority on diseases of the heart and blood vessels, has to his credit important innovations in this field.

Research by Dr. de Bakey and his associates has shown that 40 per cent of these strokes are caused by blockage of arteries in the chest or lungs and a resulting stoppage in the flow of blood to the brain. To discover the location of the damaged artery, it is necessary to take X-ray pictures of the path of an injected dye. With the site pinpointed, an operation makes it possible to replace the damaged arterial segments with plastic material.

When the flow of blood to the brain cells is resumed, the patient's symptoms—even paralysis—are relieved. Even where irreparable brain-tissue damage has occurred, the operation may minimize its effects or prevent later strokes.

A hydraulic heart

The heart functions with such precision and delicacy that its hardiness seems amazing. Yet, as we know, there are individuals who are born with defective hearts or who develop defects later in life. In former times such defects eventually proved fatal. Nowadays skilled surgeons can correct them by daring heart surgery.

Direct surgery on any portion of the heart calls for use of a mechanical heart and lungs during the operation. All these pumping

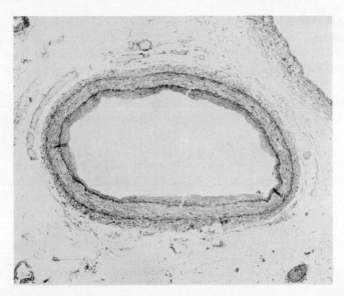

ARTERY DETERIORATION: (Above) Cross-section of a normal artery which provides a clear channel for the blood flow. (Below) Fatty deposits have formed and hardened in the artery, steadily narrowing the channel. If a blood clot forms in the affected artery, serious damage will result.

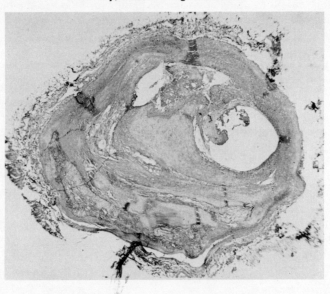

HEART-LUNG MACHINE: In certain kinds of heart operations it is necessary to give the heart and lungs a rest. The machine pictured here takes over the pumping and oxygenating functions of these organs. The patient's blood is passed through a series of cleverly designed rotating metal disks enclosed in a glass container. This arrangement functions as a lung substitute. The observer is able to scrutinize the color and flow of the blood throughout the course of the operation. The oxygenator has been used with satisfactory results in hundreds of operations.

arrangements are of the most extraordinary complexity and require the greatest care and ingenuity in avoiding any mechanical breakdown during the operation. Engineers and designers at the Convair Division of General Dynamics Corporation have designed one of the cleverest of these "heart-lung" machines.

This device applies pump action to four Plexiglas chambers, each of which contains a rubber bladder that works like one of the four chambers in the heart. These bladders work in pairs, like the two ventricles and the two auricles. The contraction and expansion of these bladders is keyed to a definite rhythm, as in a normally functioning heart.

In another chamber, which is filled with oxygen and takes the place of the lungs, the blood is oxygenated by passing it in a thin film over screens. One of the most remarkable features of this magnificent piece of equipment is its ingenious servomechanisms for automatically controlling the oxygenation and acidity of the blood.

Electronic pacemakers for ailing hearts

When the heart is functioning normally, the upper chamber (the auricles) and the lower chamber (the ventricles) are connected by muscles that contain nerve fibers. The beating of the upper chamber stimulates the lower chamber to contract; the result is a normal, satisfactory heartbeat that takes place 100,000 times a day.

If the muscular connection is interrupted for any reason, the auricles and ventricles operate independently of each other. Thus, after a successful heart operation the auricles may produce impulses that are too feeble to activate the ventricles. This condition is known as "heart block." Such a block can sharply reduce the flow of blood to the brain and other vital organs. There is also a possibility that the lower chamber may stop beating altogether. If the condition persists, it usually proves fatal.

The problem, then, is how to step up the heartbeat by artificial means. Since the heart impulse is electrical, scientists reasoned that it could be aided by an electrical "pacemaker." They accomplish this in the following way. After the patient has been given a local anesthetic, his chest is pierced with a hollow needle. A very fine wire is passed through the needle and embedded in the heart muscle. A second wire is attached to the skin.

A transistor amplifier, powered by small portable batteries, is attached to the outer ends of the wires. The amplifier causes the auricles to pump more strongly and thus raises the patient's heartbeat to normal. A tiny amplifier, weighing two ounces, can run for a month before the batteries have to be recharged. A larger amplifier, weighing two pounds, can run for four months.

This technique can be used during heart operations. It has also been made available to people whose hearts have been weakened by such ailments as rheumatic heart disease.

A computer for forecasting heart disease

Heart disease in various forms kills over 800,000 Americans every year. It is therefore important for the medical profession to develop new diagnostic methods that will enable doctors to spot potential cases long before they reach the acute-danger stage.

Through the use of an IBM computer, experts at the New York University–Bellevue Medical Center are able to prophesy the likelihood of a heart attack in early middle age. This method involves feeding mathematical information about physique, blood chemistry and heredity into the computer. In a few minutes the computer completes complicated calculations which ordinarily would take weeks.

The value of this method, aside from its usefulness for research purposes, is that it offers the opportunity for corrective action, such as adopting a moderate diet, avoiding excessive strain and stress, or instituting a healthful regime of exercise.

Diagnosing heart ailments with radioisotopes is discussed on page 168.

CANCER

There are half a million new cancer cases in the United States every year. Its annual toll of victims is about half that number.

Lung cancer is increasing much more rapidly than any other form of the disease. It kills 35,000 Americans every year—85 per cent of them men. Dr. John Roderick Heller, director of the National Cancer Institute, states: "Statistical evidence, supported by laboratory findings, has shown that excessive cigarette smoking can be a cause of lung cancer, and that the greater the consumption of cigarettes, the greater the risk." The death rate from lung cancer among heavy smokers is 23 times greater than among non-smokers.

Actually "cancer" is a very loose term. There are almost 300 known types of cancer in human beings. But 30 common types take in 90 per cent of the cases. As the cancer spreads, the diseased cells absorb more than their share of cell nourishment. They can grow and increase even in a starving man; or they can in effect cause a victim to starve.

Causes

Most authorities agree that cells become cancerous through mutation (sudden departures from the parent type).

Inherited defective genes. This is rare. However, heredity may

ANIMAL RESEARCH: At the Pfizer Laboratory in Maywood, New Jersey, tumors are implanted in animals in order to study the effect of various drugs on the progress of the disease. "Poochie," the pet of the laboratory, is so fascinated by the calculator that he always heads for it whenever let out of his basket.

make some people susceptible to attack, and make others resistant to the disease.

Radiation. This may come from X-radiation, gamma rays or too much ultraviolet light. Overexposure to strong sunlight may lead to cancer in some cases; the same result may follow repeated exposure to atomic radiation or X-rays.

Harmful chemicals. A good many tars and other chemicals are considered cancer causes. The tars from cigarette smoke have produced cancers on the skins of experimental animals. Air pollution, especially in cities, has also become suspect. The United States Public Health Service is undertaking a study of the role played by auto exhausts in causing or contributing to cancer and other ailments. According to Mark D. Hollis, chief of the sanitary engineering division, "Marked statistical associations between air pollution and many forms of heart disease and cancer have been noted . . . Auto exhausts have been demonstrated to contain cancer-producing substances."

Prolonged irritation of tissues (as in the case of a badly fitted dental plate), can lead to cancer.

Invasion by viruses. There is a widely held theory that viruses cause some types of cancer, but so far there has been no definite proof. There are tantalizing indications that viruses strongly resemble the genes (transmitters of inherited traits) in size and chemical composition. Both are made up of those fundamental but complex substances known as nucleic acids. "We have reached the point, indeed," Dr. Gilbert J. Dalldorf has observed, "where it is quite as reasonable to think of viruses as infectious genes, genes on the loose, as microparasites that may function as genes." Cancer, according to this view, is what happens after viruses seize control of the cell's heredity mechanism.

Procedures against cancer

For years the standard procedure against cancer was surgical removal of infected organs and areas, as well as irradiation of cancerous cells. Thanks to constant improvement in techniques, more and more lives are being saved. Surgeons have devised operations that were formerly considered impossible. Radiation methods have been improved with huge X-ray machines, atom smashers, atomic isotopes and nuclear reactors. (See page 165.)

But even these methods do not answer the need for a more basic attack on cancer.

Drugs against cancer

Chemotherapy—the use of anti-cancer drugs—may eventually supply the desired solution. Theoretically there are about a million chemical substances that need to be checked for their possible potency against cancer. So far, out of the many thousands that have been studied, about 70 have been found that lengthen the lives of cancer sufferers and decrease their physical discomfort. These achievements have their unquestionable value, but the trouble with all the drugs discovered thus far is that their effect is not lasting; sooner or later, the disease gains the upper hand.

The quest for a cure

In the United States, chemical substances from many parts of the world are being sifted by scientists who are patiently studying their anti-cancer properties. Some of these compounds are familiar drugs; others come from exotic plants never previously studied.

The first step is to implant cancers in mice. Three different kinds of cancer are tried in this process. Most drugs prove useless. The few that show promise are again tried on infected animals.

About 500 drugs have passed these preliminary screening tests. The drugs are then applied again—to more mice, and then on rats, dogs and other animals. These tests build up a picture of how the drugs attack the cancer cells; what effects, good or bad, they produce; what dosages of the drugs are most useful.

The tests of a single promising drug may take as long as 16 months. By this time, only one drug out of a thousand is left; the others are too weak to do an effective job on the cancer cells, or else so powerful that they harm healthy cells.

Hopeful developments

So far about 70 anti-cancer drugs of varying effectiveness have made their appearance. The solution is elusive because cancer cells exposed to a drug gradually develop a resistance to it. There is also this dilemma: if small doses are used, the cancer cells have time to build up resistance. If massive doses are tried in order to kill the

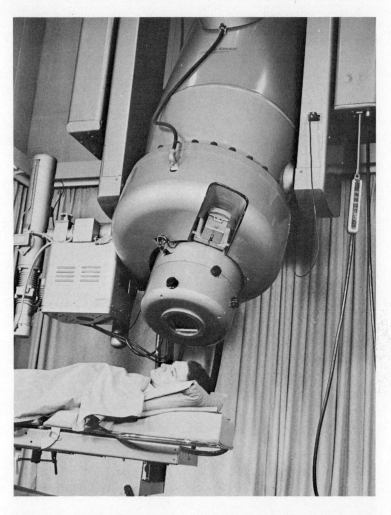

GIANT X-RAY MACHINE: A patient at the National Cancer Institute, Bethesda, Maryland, is given radiation treatment with a high-voltage X-ray machine capable of producing 2 million electron volts.

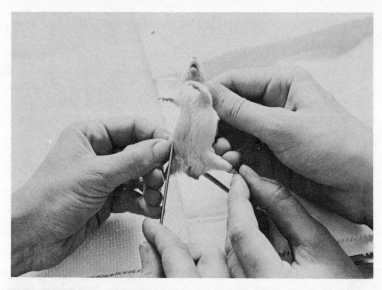

MAN'S BEST FRIENDS: (Above) In a cancer research laboratory hundreds of mice have tumors implanted daily to enable investigators to learn more about how to treat cancer.

QUEST FOR AN ANTI-CANCER AGENT: Tests of infected animals have revealed the presence of an anti-tumor agent. A laboratory technician distills an antibiotic broth to concentrate this substance. Eventually it may become possible to isolate the substance and ascertain its chemical composition.

cancer cells, then the drug will prove harmful to the rest of the body as well.

Some investigators proceed on the principle that certain substances tend to concentrate in specific tissues. Iodine, for example, heads for the thyroid gland. Applying this theory to the fight against cancer calls for a substance that would head for the diseased cells without affecting the rest of the body. By using radioactive isotope "tracers," researchers can discover the location of these substances.

One hopeful development is the discovery that the tetracycline antibiotics concentrate in the tissues of certain kinds of tumors. This has been found to apply both to animals and human beings.

By combining the antibiotic with a radioactive material, it becomes possible to locate the tumor and treat it at the same time.

This research is still in its early stages, but it presents two encouraging possibilities. One is that it will become feasible to diagnose

MASS FILTRATION: Micro-organisms have been grown in nutrient broths which are here filtered under vacuum in order to extract the broth, removing the micro-organisms. The broths are then analyzed to see if they contain an anti-cancer agent which might have been secreted by the organisms during the growth process.

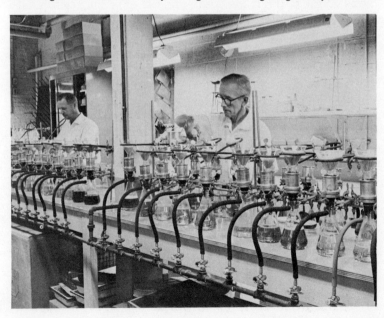

cancers when they are in the beginning, localized phase and therefore easiest to treat. Secondly, it may prove possible to use an effective drug which, guided by radioactive substances, will attack only diseased cells and leave the healthy cells intact.

Another recent hopeful development comes from a wholly different approach. Inspired by studies indicating that electricity affects cell growth, research teams at Johns Hopkins University have shown that weak, painless electrical currents applied to cancers implanted in mice have resulted in a clearing up of the diseased area. This technique will undoubtedly undergo many refinements and improvements.

Basic research

The need for a cancer cure is so urgent that it naturally absorbs the efforts of many scientists in the field of medical research. But in many departments of science, some of the most far-reaching results come from basic theoretical research that does not seem to have immediate practical value.

An example of this is seen in the problem of keeping animal cells alive in laboratory cultures. In the past, blood serum or embryo juices have been used as the culture medium. But the trouble with using these substances is that they contain large numbers of unidentified chemicals. Consequently it has been impossible for researchers to discover just what fundamental substances are needed to keep cells alive.

Dr. Charity Weymouth, a woman scientist at the Roscoe B. Jackson Memorial Laboratory at Bar Harbor, Maine, has discovered a combination of completely identified chemical substances that nourish cells in laboratory growth. These chemicals include ordinary table salt, dextrose (a form of sugar) and nine vitamins. What has this to do with cancer?

According to the American Cancer Society, "Dr. Weymouth's culture medium opens the way to precise studies of the basic chemistry of life. It will permit scientists to learn how nature uses simple salts, amino acids, glucose and hypoxanthine to produce the complicated chemicals of life."

Eventually investigators will be able to determine whether they can stop the growth of cancer cells by changing their food supply or by introducing cancer-directed poisons into their diet. By a further refinement of this process, it might become possible to find out how to use a diet that would kill cancerous cells without harming healthy cells.

ARTHRITIS

Of all crippling diseases, rheumatoid arthritis is the worst, and the most widespread in the United States. In this country it claims some 2,000,000 sufferers, many of them confined to bed or wheelchair.

The disease attacks the joints, causing stiffness and swelling accompanied by excruciating pain. Despite years of intensive research, the cause of arthritis is still unknown. Its onset is mysterious and its course unpredictable: it may sometimes let up without any treatment, and yet become progressively worse in other cases despite the most solicitous care of the patient.

The presence of the disease can be recognized by a laboratory test. The blood of an arthritic causes a solution of sheep cells to "agglutinate," or clump together.

Some years ago the drugs cortisone and ACTH were hailed as "wonder drugs" in the treatment of arthritis. However, neither of these substances has lived up to its promise. Nor are any of the other drugs used against arthritis wholly satisfactory. To the extent that they are effective, they attack only the symptoms and not the cause.

Aspirin, perhaps the most familiar and most widely used of all drugs, is still the commonest measure against arthritis. It eases aches and pains and somewhat relieves the stiffness of the joints. In some cases, when taken in the early stages, it even reduces inflammation. Unfortunately aspirin has an effect only as long as it is used; as soon as it is withdrawn, all the painful symptoms reappear with their former intensity.

Gold salts are also administered, but to a much lesser extent than aspirin. It is believed that the gold salts, when lodged in the tissues, bring about some chemical change that helps the patient; but no one knows just what this effect is. In any event, the salts operate by a slow process—it may take three months of injections to show some progress.

Phenylbutazone is a more recently used drug which has been

studied patiently with little fanfare, in order to avoid arousing false hopes. Its effectiveness is hard to gauge, as some patients respond to it favorably, while others do not benefit and in addition experience harmful side effects.

Chloroquine, a drug developed for malaria cases during World War II, has been recommended for arthritis sufferers as well. Dr. Arthur W. Bagnall, Associate Professor of Medicine at the University of British Columbia, made a four-year clinical study of the effects of giving chloroquine to arthritis sufferers. "There was a marked improvement," he reported, "in joint movement without pain in two-thirds of the patients."

In Dr. Bagnall's opinion, arthritis is "a disease of stress and strain, especially emotional." Later research, especially by Dr. Arthur L. Scherbel of the Cleveland Clinic, seems to bear out this point of view. Dr. Scherbel suggests that arthritis patients suffer from mental disturbances caused by a chemical defect in the central nervous system. He views this chemical defect as part of the disease process.

Dr. Scherbel suspects a connection between arthritis and lack of ability to tolerate stressful situations. His findings have stimulated a search for drugs that will relieve depression and also relieve the physical effects of arthritis.

POLIO

There was rejoicing all over the world in 1954 when Dr. Jonas Salk's killed-virus vaccine against poliomyelitis proved its worth in a series of extensive and searching tests. It seemed that man had at last conquered one of the most dreaded of all epidemic diseases.

Despite some confusion and mishaps, early results were very satisfactory. Analysis of the 1956 polio outbreak in Chicago, for example, unearths some interesting figures. Among those who had received no shots, the rate per 100,000 who contracted polio was 358.4; for those with one shot, the rate was 154.4; for those with two shots, 14.2. Among those who had three shots, no cases were reported.

In 1954, just before the country-wide introduction of the Salk vaccine, some 39,000 polio cases were reported all over the United States. In 1955, the first year in which the Salk vaccine was used on

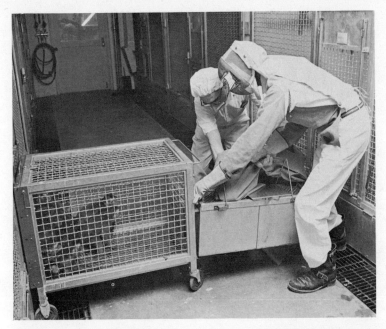

SAFEGUARDS AGAINST INFECTION: Polio vaccine is prepared from fresh kidney tissue taken from monkeys kept under the care of veterinarians. Periodic inspections and spotless cleanliness are part of the precautions against the possibility of infection.

a large scale, the number of cases dropped to 5,500. In 1958, however, the number rose to 6,000; and a similar number was projected for 1959.

The earliest figures assembled for 1957 showed that the paralytic polio rate for vaccinated persons was 75 per cent lower than for those who had received no injections. A year later, however, paralytic polio was on the rise and this tendency has continued.

While the experience with the killed-virus vaccine has been good, it has not been quite as good as was originally anticipated. There are a number of reasons for this, the chief one being the appalling indifference of the American public.

As of the first half of 1959, 98,000,000 Americans had received no shots, while another 12,000,000 had received only one or two shots — three being considered essential for immunity. The 40-and-under

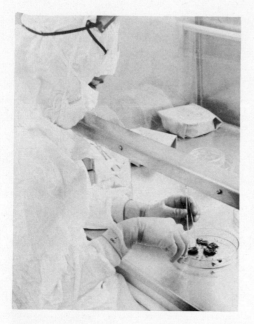

CUTTING OPERATION: The laboratory technician who cuts up and minces the monkey kidneys is dressed in a surgical gown, a mask, gloves and disposable footwear. The walls, floors, tables and equipment are frequently treated with antiseptics, and daily tests are made to verify that the area is remaining sterile.

age group is particularly susceptible to polio. In the past, only 2 per cent of the polio cases occurred in persons over 40. Yet, as of May 1959, one-third of the 40-and-under age group in the United States had received no injections.

The 5- to 19-year-olds have the best showing, with 70 per cent having received three shots, and only 15 per cent having received none. On the other hand, the 20-to-40 group contains 58 per cent who have received no shots and only 31 per cent who have received three.

Meanwhile there has been a great deal of lively discussion comparing the merits of vaccine made from killed virus and that from live virus. Those authorities who recommend the latter type have advanced some strong arguments.

Such a vaccine uses strains of virus that have been weakened to the extent of no longer having the power to cause polio, while still retaining the ability to stimulate the formation of antibodies in the blood stream to fight off the disease in all three forms (Types I, II and III).

As far back as 1957 the World Health Organization pointed out that preliminary tests of live-virus vaccine "failed to reveal any signs of illness or other harmful effects either in the persons vaccinated or in members of their families." Authorities who favor the live-virus vaccine feel strongly that it would do a much better job against paralytic polio than the Salk killed-virus vaccine. They add that the live-virus vaccine gives longer protection than the Salk vaccine, which may require booster shots as frequently as once a year.

Another point is that the expense involved has probably discouraged a large number of people from taking the recommended number of three killed-virus injections. Administering the live virus — in a spoonful of syrup, for example — would be much cheaper.

INSPECTING A TISSUE CULTURE OF POLIO VIRUS: After the three types of polio virus have been kept in deep freeze, they are added to individual tissue cultures. The specialist inspects the tissue cultures, from which a virus-carrying fluid is then filtered off. The virus is now inactivated and subjected to an exhaustive series of tests. Finally all three virus strains are combined into a single vaccine.

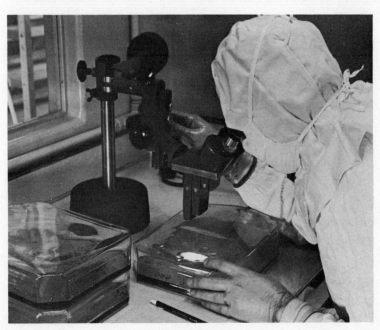

It would cost as little as one-tenth of the killed-virus treatment. This is a very important consideration in underdeveloped areas and countries.

Another argument in favor of the live-virus vaccine is that it can be stored indefinitely in deep-freeze units. This is not true of the killed-virus vaccine. In addition, persons immunized by the killed virus can still spread the infection to others not immunized. However, those immunized by live virus cannot communicate infection.

In localities of central Africa some 250,000 persons were given doses of a live-virus vaccine developed by Dr. Hilary Koprowski of the Wistar Institute in Philadelphia. Communities which had suffered outbreaks of paralytic polio reported no further cases after receiving the vaccine. Nor were ill effects of any other kind reported.

In Minneapolis, some groups of schoolchildren received live-virus vaccine prepared by Dr. Herald Cox of the Lederle Laboratories. As of May 1959 the live-virus vaccine developed by Dr. Albert B. Sabin of the University of Cincinnati had been safely administered to 4,500,000 persons in Europe, Africa and Asia with satisfactory results.

As far as the United States is concerned, the United States Public Health Service takes an understandably cautious attitude toward the adoption of the live-virus vaccine. Before the Health Service agrees to nationwide use of live virus, it must be satisfied that:

The results achieved with already vaccinated persons are convincing.

The live virus cannot cause disease.

A live-virus dose acts against all three types of polio.

The live virus cannot cause disease by passing from immunized to non-immunized people.

The presence of other viruses in the intestinal tract does not affect immunity to polio.

DIABETES

Proteins, the key to the life process, are the most complicated chemical substances in nature. A single human body contains almost 100,000 different kinds of proteins. Each one has a specific function. For example, insulin, a protein substance in the pancreas gland, has the job of converting carbohydrates (sugars, starches and fats) into energy and heat.

If the insulin mechanism does not work properly, unused sugars accumulate in the blood stream; the victim becomes diabetic. The presence of excess sugar overworks the kidneys; the body's metabolism is disturbed; proteins are destroyed by conversion to sugar. Other consequences may be: hardening of the arteries; deterioration of eyesight; infections of various kinds. The course of the disease, if unchecked by treatment, leads to coma and death.

In 1921 the epoch-making isolation of insulin by Doctors F. G. Banting, H. C. Best, and J. R. Macleod made it possible to administer insulin by daily injections to diabetes sufferers. By compensating for the patient's lack of natural insulin, the injections enable him to live a fairly normal life.

Because proteins make up most of the active parts of all living organisms, these substances are of enormous interest to research scientists. To know the composition and structure of the proteins is vitally important. Until very recently this knowledge seemed impossible to obtain.

Chemists know that proteins are made up of chains or cables of simpler units — the amino acids. There are 24 of these, and they have been called "the alphabet of life." Each type of protein molecule is unique in the kinds of amino acid units it contains and in the way they are arranged.

For years chemists vainly attempted to break down the protein molecules. They succeeded in separating and counting the amino acid units, but they were baffled when it came to analyzing the structural arrangement.

At Cambridge University in England, a team of investigators led by Dr. Frederick Sanger worked for ten years on the insulin molecule. At last, in 1954, they succeeded in piecing together the structure of this molecule, which is comparatively one of the simplest protein substances. They found that the insulin molecule is made up of 17 different amino acids. These are part of two chains, one of which contains 21 acid units while the other contains 30. The units are joined together by sulphur atoms.

To summarize the patient labors of the Sanger team very briefly, they broke the insulin molecule into smaller parts and treated some of the amino acid units with DNP (dinitrophenyl). The DNP stained these units yellow and thus gave a clue to their relative location. By use of the same technique it finally became possible to locate the position of all 51 units and reassemble all the fragments in their proper places in the molecule. For this magnificent achievement, which will eventually make it possible to learn the secret of the more complicated protein substances, Dr. Sanger received a Nobel Prize in 1958.

Other investigators have devoted considerable research to the problem of attacking diabetes with some drug that can be taken by mouth, thus making injections unnecessary. Two anti-diabetic drugs have achieved a considerable amount of success, although results vary with the condition of each individual.

One of these oral drugs is DNB (phenformin), which stimulates the blood tissues to use blood sugar without the aid of insulin. The other oral drug is chlorpropamide (Diabinese), which works by stimulating extra liberation of insulin. Conservative opinion holds that it may take another 15 years to achieve thoroughly satisfactory results with oral drugs; but there is justified hope that in time they will completely replace treatment by injection.

MENTAL ILLNESS

Under the stress of modern conditions, cases of mental illness have risen to fantastic proportions. According to even the most optimistic figures, one out of every 16 Americans will be afflicted, during his lifetime, with some form of mental disease.

The most widespread of these ailments is schizophrenia, in which the victim retreats from reality and lives in a private fantasy world of hallucinations and delusions. It affects three out of every thousand people in the general population; half the beds in mental hospitals are occupied by schizophrenics. Each year 150,000 new victims enter the mental hospitals.

The cause of schizophrenia is not known; psychiatrists consider it "the most urgent and at the same time most baffling question confronting them." Up to the very recent past, attempts to treat schizophrenia have been trapped in a blind alley.

In recent years, however, many research scientists have turned to

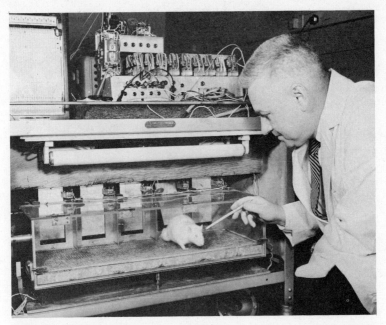

PROBLEM-SOLVING EXPERIMENTS: This apparatus was specially devised to study the reactions of animals in problem-solving experiments. Both young and old rats are used, to see what effects may be due to age differences. In order to make the findings more meaningful, the animals are kept free of physical or emotional stress.

the idea of attacking mental illness through chemistry. The famous geneticist, Linus Pauling, explains the idea underlying this trend: "I am sure that most mental disease is chemical in origin, and that the chemical abnormalities involved are usually the result of abnormalities in the genetic constitution of the individual."

Dr. Mark Altschule, Assistant Clinical Professor of Medicine at Harvard Medical School, is one of the outstanding men in this rapidly growing field. He is interested, as he puts it, in "showing that by modifying the biochemistry of a patient, you can modify the patient."

Research indicated that schizophrenia sufferers have excessively active adrenal glands, and that slowing down this activity would bring about an improvement in their condition. Eventually they

TESTING A NEW DRUG: As part of a series of experiments to test Niamid, this rat is being weighed after being given the drug. Niamid is intended for use in treating depressed patients.

found that a serum prepared from the pineal gland was suitable for the purpose. (The pineal gland is a tiny organ, shaped like a pine cone, located in the brain.)

However, the size of this gland poses a real problem. In order to obtain enough of the extract to supply a single patient for one day,

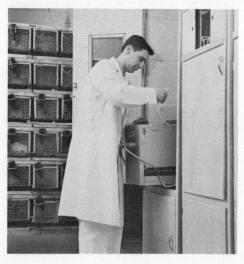

THE TEST STARTS: The rat is placed in a specially designed laboratory box which contains levers, a food dispenser and a mild electric-shock grid. The rat's performance is recorded on an elaborate relay panel board and at the same time it is plotted on an automatic graphing instrument.

PUSHING THE LEVER: In the course of the experiment the rat discovers that by pushing a lever it can sometimes obtain food, while other times pushing the lever will avoid a mild shock. At other times, pushing the lever will have no effect at all.

the pineal glands of 15 steers are required. It may prove feasible to use the pineal glands of whales for this purpose.

Dt. Altschule's original experiments were promising, yet ultimately disheartening. At first patients showed marked improvement on receiving the extract; but after a short period they relapsed into their previous condition. Painstaking study revealed that a protein substance in the extract caused the patient gradually to become immune to it.

A great deal of hard work then went into a series of complicated separation processes which eventually yielded a protein-free extract. In its improved form, the serum produced excellent results, but much still remains to be done. The next step is an attempt to produce a stable, standardized serum. Then, after careful testing on thousands of patients, the improved extract will be ready for general use.

Dr. Altschule believes the serum will be most effective with patients in the early stages of schizophrenia. There is reason to believe that cures will be permanent because this serum will change the patient's physical condition by changing his metabolism.

A study of schizophrenics by scientists at Tulane University showed that their blood serum contains a substance called taxarein. When this serum was injected into the blood stream of convict volunteers, "the injections induced behavior changes which were very similar to the pattern of behavior of the patients from whom the blood was taken." The effect of the injection wore off in about two hours.

A later experiment with rats at the Merck Institute for Therapeutic Research at West Point, Pennsylvania, showed similar results. The experiment called for three groups of animals. One group received injections of blood plasma from mentally normal persons; a second group had injections from a group of physically ill people. The remaining group received injections of the blood plasma of mentally ill people, mostly schizophrenics.

The animals had been trained to climb a five-foot rope for a food reward. The performance of the control groups was far superior to that of the group which had received injections of the blood of mentally ill persons.

"The data," the institute's scientists reported, "established beyond doubt that plasma from psychotic patients affects the performance of our trained rats." These experiments support the theory that a substance present in the blood of psychotic persons will cause other human beings or animals to become temporarily psychotic. Further research should eventually identify this substance and explain how it works.

In recent years there has been a great deal of research into the effect of drugs on mentally ill persons in the hope of bringing about complete or partial cures by chemical means. Some of these drugs are tranquilizers, intended to have a calming effect on patients who are unduly agitated. Others, termed "psychic energizers," have precisely the opposite purpose; they act against states of deep depression.

TEST RESULTS: On completion of the test, a research assistant uses the figures registered on the control panel (see page 78) to evaluate the test animal's performance. The record shows how many times the rat received a shock, how many times it received food after pressing the lever, and other results. Experiments of this kind enable scientists to appraise the effect of different drugs on an animal's behavior.

One of the most interesting drugs of the latter group is phenelzine (trade name, Nardil). It is derived from hydrazine, a hydrogen-nitrogen compound which was one of the basic fuel components of the German V-2 rockets of World War II.

The particular merit of this drug, at least in its early tests, is that it showed no harmful side effects. Extensive use of Nardil at the Western State Hospital, Fort Steilacom, Washington, resulted in the discharge, as recovered, of 80 per cent of the patients within 60 to 90 days of beginning treatment with the drug. The remaining patients also experienced varying degrees of improvement. These results are encouraging but need to be followed up by more extensive testing.

Another approach to the problem of mental illness is the theory that some forms of mental illness may be due to an imbalance of chemical substances in the brain. An excess of the hormone serotonin in the brain, for example, slows transmission in the brain's nerve circuits. This results in hallucinations.

The research laboratories in neuropsychiatry of the Veterans Administration are experimenting with volunteers to study the effects of excess serotonin. By shedding light on the mechanism of hallucination this research may lead to better diagnosis and more effective treatment of mental illness.

Relieving severe depression by "atomic surgery" is discussed on page 168.

BLOOD TECHNIQUES

In recent years, scientific study of the human blood system has made remarkable progress. Diagnostic methods have become incredibly delicate and detailed. Blood ailments which once used to bring on quick and unavoidable death are now successfully treated by a variety of ingenious techniques.

Electronic analysis of fats

Many studies made by biochemists have indicated that a diet which contains a large amount of saturated fats may result in an increase of the fatty-substance (cholesterol) content of the blood. (Saturated fats are those which are solid at room temperature.) There is considerable evidence that points to such an increase resulting in hardening of the arteries and heart disease. (See page 52.)

On the other hand, other studies seem to indicate that a diet which sticks to unsaturated fats (those that are liquid at room temperature) may result in a reduced cholesterol content in the blood. To draw foolproof conclusions from both types of studies, it is necessary to know what happens to fats in the body, and what effect they have on the blood.

Dr. Seymour A. Lipsky of the Yale University School of Medicine has designed an electronic instrument to "separate the individual components of the blood and tissues with greater facility than any device heretofore available." The result will be, he believes, "to shed new light on the composition, synthesis, breakdown and transport of these substances in the body."

If this apparatus proves effective, it should conclusively demonstrate what effect fatty substances have on the blood. This research may in turn point the way to processing foods that will have a low saturated-fat content. This might well lead to an enormous decrease in the number of deaths from heart disease.

Enzyme "X"

One of the most baffling forms of hypertension (high blood pressure) is essential hypertension. This is a form of high blood pressure unaccompanied by any noticeable deterioration of the heart and arteries.

A five-year study at the Hypertension Clinic at Mount Sinai Hospital, New York, promises to shed light on this mystery. Research showed that the hormone norepinephrine, released by the nerve endings, causes blood vessels to constrict and thus forces an increase in blood pressure. It is known that under normal conditions this hormone is broken up by certain enzymes, preventing an increase in blood pressure.

The research group theorizes that sufferers from essential hypertension lack the enzymes which break up the hormone. If this is confirmed, it will explain an older theory that heredity plays a role in high blood pressure.

Another mystery that would be solved is the tantalizing problem of why emotional states heighten blood pressure in some people and not in others. The explanation would be that those who lack the enzyme in their body system are the ones whose blood pressure is raised by emotional stress.

The next step is to isolate the enzyme and administer it to individuals who suffer from high blood pressure. The observed results would enable the researchers to verify the effect of the synthetic enzyme on victims of essential hypertension.

Diagnosing a drop of blood

Studies by Dr. Winston Price and his associates at Johns Hopkins University point to the possibility of being able to diagnose cancer, heart disease and many other ailments (including mental disease) from a single drop of blood.

The technique depends on the fact that the blood serum can be fractionated (broken down) into definite patterns. The serum of normally healthy individuals reveals a characteristic pattern. Similarly, each kind of disease has its own specific, unique pattern in blood serum.

What is particularly valuable about this method is that it can reveal the presence of disease in its early stages, at a point where conventional diagnosis is unable to unearth any clinical symptoms. If developed further, this method will make it possible to treat diseases at their inception, thus making cure and recovery much more likely. This would be particularly valuable in the diagnosis of cancer and mental illness, where the possibilities of cure are strongly dependent on early diagnosis.

The research studies in this field are still tentative, and much still remains to be done before the technique is established as conclusive and dependable.

Stapling blood vessels

In the treatment of accidents and in much major surgery, the problem of fastening together the disconnected ends of arteries and large veins has been a serious one. In most cases, the blood vessels have to be stitched together laboriously and delicately with a fine thread.

Russian surgeons have solved the difficulty effectively by reconnecting the severed blood vessels with a stapling gun. Actually this is not the familiar stapling machine we know. The surgical stapling is done with a highly intricate gadget, about five inches long, which comes in some 40 different, highly specialized models.

To use this method, the surgeon must be able to work with severed blood vessels having free ends about three-quarters of an inch long. The machine grasps each end, turns back a part of each to make a "cuff," and then connects the cuffs with wire staples made of tantalum.

The process has several advantages over the use of thread. In the first place, the stapling procedure is much quicker. Secondly, the staples, unlike thread, never cause irritation. Finally, the inside bore of the stapled blood vessel retains its original size, so that the blood can flow through unimpeded.

Dacron blood vessels

Up to very recent times, it has been difficult and costly to replace diseased blood vessels. The sources were grafts and human tissue.

Research at the Meadox Weaving Corporation of Haledon, New Jersey, called for a synthetic fabric that would meet several requirements: it would be durable; it would not allow excessive blood leakages; and it would be thin enough to permit normal cell tissues to regrow inside and outside the synthetic blood vessel. After six months of intensive experiments, a very finely woven Dacron proved satisfactory. Between 1955 and 1958 over 1,500 of these synthetic blood vessels were implanted in human beings with successful results.

A potent hormone

When the kidneys are not working properly, the result is sometimes the formation of the hormone angiotonin in the blood stream. This hormone comes in two forms, one of which is so potent in causing hypertension that much less than a gram of it would be enough to raise the blood pressure of 166,000 people.

Up to very recently it was almost impossible to study the way in which this hormone works, as it is virtually unobtainable from animal sources. However, a research team at the Cleveland Clinic Research Division has succeeded in preparing angiotonin synthetically, which opens the way for at last finding out how this powerful hormone operates.

Artificial kidneys

The action of the kidneys in filtering wastes from the blood system is essential to maintain the living process. Various causes can bring kidney function to a halt, with quick death as a result. Among these causes are: severe shock with heavy loss of blood; serious infections; quick-acting poisons.

To handle serious emergencies, doctors have devised artificial kidneys. Dr. Willem Johan Kolff of the Cleveland Clinic has designed a particularly effective model. It is a stainless-steel tub, 24 inches across and 17 inches high. The merit of this device is that it does away with movable parts that are expensive as well as time-consuming to set up in situations where every second counts. In fact, the most important part of the machine is a disposable unit of cellophane and plastic wire which costs $59.

To operate the artificial kidney, the patient is stretched out beside the machine, which has been filled with two pints of blood containing heparin (to prevent clotting). Polyethylene tubes connect the core of the artificial kidney to the patient's radial artery (located in the wrist). Veins in the patient's elbows are linked up to cellophane tubes in the machine.

The patient's poisoned blood flows through the core of the machine, where a pump bathes the tubing in a chemical bath which matches the salinity and acidity of healthy blood. The tubing is just porous enough to let the abnormally poisonous content seep into the more diluted chemical bath outside. (The tubing must not be porous enough to allow the blood cells and protein molecules to escape.) The separation of the poisons may take as much as six hours, but when the artificial kidney's rinsing work has been accomplished, the patient's life has been saved—the poisons have been removed.

New blood for old

Blood is made up of plasma (the liquid part) and the red blood cells. Recent research has improved on the methods of removing blood, separating the plasma, and returning the red blood cells to the donor. The whole process, known as plasmapheresis, takes 20 minutes. There are several advantages to this technique, which has been developed effectively by Joseph Stokes Jr. and Joseph Smolens of the University of Pennsylvania School of Medicine.

In the first place, since the body can regenerate its plasma within 24 hours, donors can give blood more frequently. Single sterile plasmas obtained in this way enormously increase the stock of gamma globulin and other vital plasma fractions which give immunity against various diseases.

By immunizing normally healthy donors against mumps virus, whooping cough, diphtheria and tetanus, antibodies can be obtained from them in much larger quantities than heretofore. Up to now, horse serums have been used against these diseases. But animal serum sometimes produces harmful effects which will be eliminated by using human immunity-serums.

Nor is this all. The blood stream of some individuals becomes poisoned for various reasons. Now this poisoned blood can be removed and replaced by healthy blood from a normal donor. As Drs. Stokes and Smolens point out, this process makes it possible to remove poisoned blood from an individual's body, "with continuous return of his own red blood cells and of another donor's plasma." Application of this technique to almost a thousand cases, they continue, "may be said to have already assured its broad usefulness in eliminating certain materials which are harmful to the body and of which the body cannot rapidly rid itself."

It is even conceivable that this process can eventually be used to check the aging process. For one of the factors in aging is the accumulation of poisonous substances in the blood which the body cannot eliminate. The removal of an aging individual's blood and the substitution of healthy blood would prevent the deterioration which now takes place.

VACCINES, CHEMOTHERAPY AND ANTIBIOTICS

Vaccines

High up on the list of recent beneficial and ingenious scientific achievements is the discovery that man's worst enemies, the microorganisms, can be used to stimulate the formation of antibodies which will prevent these organisms from multiplying. The search for new and improved vaccines is a never-ending struggle, and each year brings its story of patient, resourceful toil, with some magnificent successes as well as disappointing failures.

A vaccine for measles

The virus that causes measles is so elusive that the disease has long been considered unavoidable. However, it often involves severe complications and is particularly dangerous for children under three years of age and for adults. In fact, it now results in more fatalities than polio. That is why virologists have sought to develop a vaccine for measles despite the technical difficulties involved.

Man is apparently the only natural host for the measles virus.

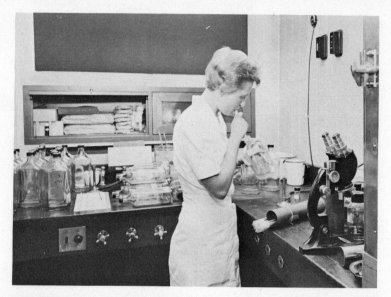

DEVELOPING A NEW VACCINE: Viruses grown in bottles are removed for preparation of a new vaccine that proved successful in reducing respiratory infections among military recruits.

Monkeys are the only animals that can be infected with it. Dr. John F. Enders of Harvard Medical School, who received a Nobel Prize for his work in growing the polio virus on monkey kidney tissue, returned to the measles vaccine problem after having acknowledged failure 20 years earlier.

Using modern techniques of tissue culture, Dr. Enders obtained measles virus from the throats or blood of measles patients. He grew the virus on human kidney cells, which gave him a method of measuring immunity. After breeding 72 generations of measles virus, he felt it had been weakened enough for vaccine investigation.

Inoculating healthy monkeys with the weakened virus, he found that the organisms lived for a while in the throats of the animals but were unable to multiply in their blood. Dr. Enders then turned to the problem of checking the possibility that the vaccine might cause encephalitis or brain inflammation (often a consequence of measles). Indications are that the new measles vaccine will be safe and effective.

Vaccine cocktails

Studies by the National Institutes of Health have shown that children under six suffer five times as much from respiratory ailments as persons over seventeen, and that the younger the patient is, the more severe the illness.

One test by the Laboratory of Infectious Diseases of the National Institutes showed that children under five years of age, hospitalized with respiratory infections, have about 25 times more viruses in their throats than children who have other illnesses. This critical situation points up the dangers for these children, and also indicates that they are prime sources for passing the ailments on to others.

Dr. Robert Huebner, chief virologist at the Laboratory, has suggested that the most effective way to cope with these dangers is to prepare a vaccine containing viruses of some 25 diseases. Laboratories of several leading drug houses are busy with preliminary tests of a multiple-purpose vaccine for young children. Perfecting such a vaccine should lead to a spectacular drop in virus diseases among this age group and the general population as well.

Fooling the viruses

In 1958 Dr. Alick Isaacs, head of a research team working at the laboratories of the British Medical Research Council, described the development of an anti-virus substance called Interferon.

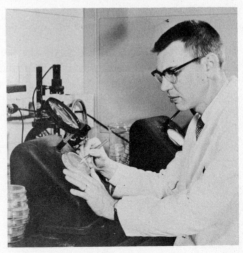

COUNTING INFECTIOUS VIRUS UNITS: The virologist grows a layer of cells in a glass dish. He adds a solution of dispersed virus particles that grow into the tissue for about an hour. The virologist then counts the holes and rings that appear as each virus uses the cell to create additional viruses.

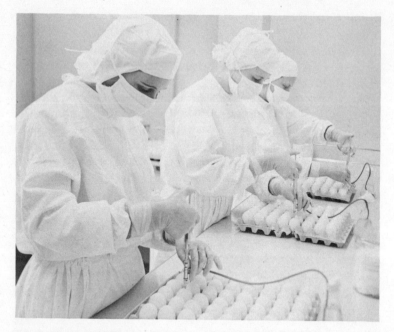

PREPARING FLU VACCINE: An egg makes a splendid nutrient medium for growing influenza viruses. Laboratory technicians drill holes in eggs, "seed" them with influenza viruses and then seal up the eggs.

The team started with the knowledge that some viruses can block the growth of other kinds of viruses. Further research showed that a protein was responsible for this effect, and that it was produced by killed viruses but not by live ones.

To see how this would work out, the investigators infected the membranes of living eggs with killed influenza viruses. They then inoculated cultures of living viruses with the products of the previous infection. The living viruses stopped multiplying. Hence the name, "Interferon."

The scientists are unable to explain precisely what happens, but they theorize about the reaction in this way. The live virus contains a substance which is essential to reproduction. Interferon (in the killed virus) has the same, or a similar, chemical composition. But it has

SAFE EXTRACTION: Before extracting the virus-laden fluid from the eggs, the technician applies a heating iron to burn through the cap of each shell, sterilizing the edges of each opening.

undergone some physical change that blocks reproduction instead of aiding it.

Considerable research remains to be done on Interferon to learn more about how it works. It is thought to be non-toxic, but this theory requires rigorous testing. In any event, Interferon promises to be the source of a safe and effective vaccine against influenza.

THE HARVEST: Inserting a suction tube in each open egg, the technician draws off the virus-bearing fluid into large glass containers. The vaccine will be prepared from this fluid.

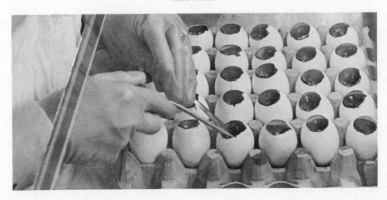

The conquest of tuberculosis

Tuberculosis was once known as "the Great White Plague." Yet the struggle to wipe it out has achieved some remarkable successes. In the United States the tuberculosis death rate has decreased in the last 60 years from an annual figure of 194 per 100,000 to 8 per 100,000.

This means an enormous saving of lives — some 300,000 every year. The battle still remains a costly one, for as recently as 1955 state and local agencies in New York State spent $50,000,000 on tuberculosis control. However, thanks to improved drugs and surgical techniques as well as better living conditions, the tuberculosis rate continues to go down.

Yet the picture hardly calls for optimism even today. There are about 250,000 known active tubercular cases, plus an estimated unknown 100,000 — and 100,000 new cases every year. Leading authorities in the field believe that the United States could make much greater progress in wiping out tuberculosis by the use of BCG, a vaccine which the Public Health Service, always extremely cautious, frowns on.

BCG (Bacillus-Calmette-Guerin) is named for two French scientists who first developed the vaccine from tubercular cattle in the 1920's. Outside the United States, BCG has been used to vaccinate about 150,000,000 persons. Such vaccination is compulsory in some countries — for example, France, Norway, Denmark, Brazil and Japan. Careful studies have shown that BCG reduces the incidence of tuberculosis by about 80 per cent.

To get the benefits of BCG in the United States, leading scientists have recommended that the vaccine be administered to doctors, nurses and family members who come in contact with tubercular patients. Likewise they feel that BCG should be given on a mass scale to persons with low resistance and those who live under unfavorable conditions in overcrowded areas. So far these projects are still in the suggestion stage.

Chemotherapy, or the quest for new drugs

All over the world thousands of "herb hunters" are searching for plants and other sources of valuable drugs. Dr. Alfred Taylor, who does cancer research at the University of Texas, has pointed out that "in plants we have more compounds than the scientists could synthesize in a thousand years. And as a rule, the naturally occurring compounds are less likely to be poisonous than the synthetic, because they have developed in association with life."

A new pain-killer

After 25 years of research a team of scientists at the National Institutes of Health developed a new pain-killing drug, tentatively labeled NIH 7519.

What made the task formidable is this: the more effective a drug is in killing pain, the more addictive it is likely to be and the more harmful its side effects will be. Yet the new drug, while ten times more powerful than morphine, is safer and less addictive.

NIH 7519 is a coal-tar derivative, belonging to a series of organic compounds known as benzomorphans. Its introduction will be particularly timely, as the decrease in opium production has resulted in a world-wide shortage of morphine for medical purposes. Aside from its medical value, the new drug is expected to be useful in curing opium addicts.

Curbing the Staphylococcus

During the years 1956-1959 a germ called the Staphylococcus aureus caused more than 500 outbreaks of infection in United States hospitals. The ailments ranged from abscesses, rashes and eye infections to blood poisoning and pneumonia. Antibiotics proved useless against these bacteria.

The infections were particularly dangerous for surgical and other severely ill patients, as well as for infants and elderly persons. The worst outbreak, at a Houston, Texas, hospital, took the lives of 16 infants.

Dr. Perry B. Hudson of the Francis Delafield Hospital in New York made a painstaking study of the hospital conditions under which germs flourished. He concluded that hospital cleaning techniques were not sufficiently thorough. The solution to the problem is a new germ-killer called Permachem. This is a combination of powerful germicidal chemicals containing tin and silver.

The new germ-killer is blended into floor wax and window-cleaning materials, sprayed on hospital furniture, walls and ceilings, mixed into laundry rinse water and impregnated into mattress covers.

When tried experimentally at a cost of 25 cents a patient per day, the new germicide proved highly successful in keeping the Staphylococcus at bay. Commercial manufacture should bring the cost down still further.

In 1957 Dr. Hamao Umezawa of Tokyo University discovered kanamycin, produced by a mold that is related to the one which produces streptomycin and neomycin. Kanamycin has turned out to be highly effective against Staphylococci and shows promise in other fields as well.

Cure for hookworm and roundworm

Throughout the world there are some 450,000,000 persons afflicted with hookworm, caused by a bloodsucking parasite. The elimination of this widespread disease is therefore one of the world's most pressing health problems.

In 1958 British scientists working in the laboratories of the Wellcome Foundation discovered a drug that promises to wipe out this scourge. The drug is an ammonium compound (bephenium hydroxynaphthoate), commercially marketed as Alcopar. When clinically tested in Ceylon, where hookworm is widespread, the drug, administered by mouth, achieved remarkably rapid cures.

Even more prevalent is a kindred disease called roundworm. In a test with children between the ages of four and ten, the results of administering Alcopar were equally encouraging. These children were severely emaciated, dehydrated and anemic. To keep them alive, doctors had to give them blood transfusions and intravenous injections. Yet after receiving large doses of the drug for four successive days, the children became well enough to be discharged from the hospital after six weeks.

Tranquilizers to overcome shock

Shock is a state in which the blood circulation fails; unless curbed in time, this dangerous condition may lead to death. According to a theory which had been discredited but is again finding acceptance, bodily injury or severe stress releases poisons that lower blood pressure to the danger point. These poisons are thought to be serotonin and histamine.

At a 1958 meeting of the American College of Surgeons, Dr.

Cyril J. Jones and Charles B. Ripstein of the Albert Einstein College of Medicine described tests in which animals were subjected to acute physical stress. Rats subjected to stress died of shock. Another group of rats subjected to the same conditions were given reserpine, chlorpromazine or other tranquilizing drugs. These animals survived, indicating to the experimenters that in the second case the drugs blocked the escape of blood fluids into the tissues, so that blood pressure was maintained.

These research findings may offer valuable leads for the treatment of patients for shock after surgery or serious accidents.

Shrinking brain tissues

There are times when it is highly desirable to shrink brain tissues — in the event of brain surgery, or to lessen the pressure from a tumor or injury. Dr. Manucher Javid of the University of Wisconsin has developed a drug which is a compound of concentrated urea and an invert sugar solution. The drug has a strongly dehydrating effect.

Though this property of concentrated urea has been known for over 30 years, its use was formerly dangerous. Dr. Javid's research has placed it on a safe footing. Several years of clinical testing by over 300 brain surgeons established the value of this technique.

A drug to remove cataracts

Cataracts are cloudy growths covering the lens of the eye. They cut down the amount of light that reaches the retina. The removal of these growths is the most common major operation in the United States, with some 200,000 patients undergoing this surgery every year.

In the past, the operating surgeon has had to apply pressure to lift off the cataract, thus incurring the danger of damaging nearby tissue. Now, thanks to the development of a drug called Alpha Chymar (Alpha chymotrypsin), the surgeon can use a simple suction device that enables him to dissolve the ligaments that hold the lens to the eye; the cataract comes off without any forcing.

The drug is a protein-digesting enzyme derived from the pancreatic glands of cattle. The action of the drug, a discovery by Dr. Joaquim Barraquer of Barcelona, has been successfully applied in 13,000 operations.

Asthma relief

The standard drug for relieving asthmatic attacks is epinephrine. When Dr. J. S. Blumenthal of the University of Minnesota Medical School undertook research to find out why some asthmatic sufferers failed to respond to the drug, he made an interesting discovery.

Dr. Blumenthal's studies indicated that epinephrine is most effective when the patient's blood is more alkaline than acid. If the blood acidity was excessive, the patient could not benefit from the drug. Dr. Blumenthal found that an intravenous injection of sodium lactate corrected this condition and enabled the victim of an asthmatic attack to get immediate relief from the standard treatment.

Reserpine specialized

Reserpine is a drug that reduces blood pressure and also acts as a tranquilizer. Since it is sometimes desirable to produce one effect and not the other, research chemists at Ciba Pharmaceutical Products have split up the drug into two distinct drugs; one form reduces blood pressure but has only one-twentieth of reserpine's tranquilizing potency; the other form is about one-fourth as effective a

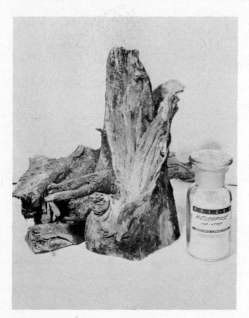

RESERPINE SOURCE: This small, woody shrub, Rauwolfia heterophylla, found in India and other tropical and semi-tropical regions, is the main source of reserpine.

tranquilizer as reserpine, but has only one-fortieth its hypotensive strength.

The search for new antibiotics

The effort to find new antibiotics has taken scientists to some queer places, but the strangest expedition of all was doubtless one to Deception Island in Antarctica. The purpose was to find out how the penguin manages to stay healthy in a region where temperatures run 100 degrees below zero and raw gales blast at more than 100 miles an hour. John McNeill Sieburth of Virginia Polytechnic Institute found that the penguin feeds on shrimp which in turn feed on plankton (microscopic marine growths). The plankton, Sieburth discovered, contains an active antibiotic that keeps the penguin hale and hearty in its bleak environment.

New form of penicillin

American and British scientists have discovered new ways of producing penicillin which will yield such advantages as these:

Producing many different forms of penicillin, each "tailor-made" to cope with specific kinds of bacteria that are at present not affected by the drug or have become resistant to it.

Modifying penicillin in order to make it suitable for people who are allergic to it.

Manufacturing penicillin synthetically—which means, eventually, more rapid and more efficient production.

At the Beecham Research Laboratories in England a group of scientists headed by Dr. G. R. Rolinson and F. P. Doyle succeeded in isolating 6-amino-penicillanic acid, the basic substance of the mold from which penicillin is derived. Professor Ernest B. Chain, who won the Nobel Prize for his work in developing penicillin, guided the research team.

The penicillin mold is made up of a basic ring of carbon, hydrogen, oxygen and nitrogen atoms, with an outer "side chain" of atoms. Thanks to the new discovery, it will be possible for chemists to make thousands of different varieties of penicillin by growing the inner ring and then adding to it any one of thousands of different kinds of penicillin by varying the composition and arrangement of the atoms in the side chain.

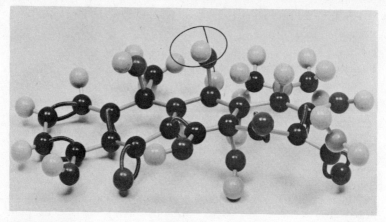

MOLECULAR MODEL: The analysis of the molecular structure of an antibiotic is extremely important, as it is essential for synthetic production. Pictured above is a model of the Terramycin molecule.

Dr. John C. Sheehan of the Massachusetts Institute of Technology achieves the same result by taking the finished product of the mold, stripping off the side chain, and substituting any desired alternative side chain. At present neither of these methods is commercially feasible, but the history of such synthetic processes is that scientists progressively simplify, refine and perfect them until the synthetic product becomes cheaper and more convenient than the natural product.

Another important advance has occurred in the synthesis in the Lederle Laboratories of one of the antibiotics in the valuable tetracycline group which includes such important antibiotics as Aureomycin, Terramycin and Achromycin.

At present the synthetic process, which calls for 30 distinct steps, is much too expensive to be commercially feasible. Yet all such achievements in synthesis are potentially important because they point the way to specialized antibiotics tailored to fit specific needs.

Overcoming penicillin allergies

A survey made from 1953 to 1957 showed that some 10 per cent of the American population suffers from allergies of various kinds. A substantial number of these persons are allergic to penicillin. In extreme cases the reaction can be quite severe.

To counteract these allergic reactions, scientists resorted to an enzyme (penicillinase) secreted by many strains of bacteria. This substance destroys the allergy-producing element in penicillin and brings complete relief from distressing side effects in anywhere from six hours to a few days. The commercial name of this substance is Neutrapen.

An antibiotic from the liver

Though highly effective against many kinds of bacteria, antibiotics are generally ineffectual against viruses. One exception is transferrin, an obscure substance found in the human liver.

In tests with mice and rats at the Harvard Medical School, investigators found that transferrin proved useful against several kinds of viruses, including two types of polio virus. This substance prevents the viruses from multiplying, and thus converts a severe illness into a mild one. One good feature of transferrin is that it does not damage normal cells.

An antibiotic from bacteria

Some fascinating research at the Presbyterian Hospital in New York points to the possibility that bacteria generally associated with human beings may turn out to be a source of effective antibiotics.

When the organism of gas gangrene is injected into mice, it kills them within 24 hours. However, an antibiotic prepared from a type of bacteria (Staphylococcus albus) generally found in the human skin, satisfactorily counteracts the otherwise deadly effects. Investigators are trying to adapt this technique to other types of infection.

Medicated bird feed

In bygone years a number of deaths resulted annually in the United States from psittacosis (also known as ornithosis or "parrot fever"). This led to a government embargo on parrots, but there are still several hundred cases a year as the disease can be caught from parakeets—or, more rarely, even from table birds, such as turkeys.

The difference nowadays is that the lives of psittacosis victims are saved by antibiotics. But a virologist, Karl F. Meyer, after a lifetime of research on bird and animal diseases, discovered an interesting way of banishing the danger; the seed fed to parakeets is impregnated with Aureomycin, which destroys the psittacosis virus. Dr.

Meyer hopes to extend the same method to preparing a medicated feed for table birds.

GENETICS

To create living matter by artificial means has long been one of the great ambitions of scientists. By using simple chemicals of the kind that are thought to have been prevalent on the earth before life appeared on it, Sidney W. Fox, a biochemist at Florida State University, has formed thousands of "spherules" with cell-like properties such as a nucleus and a membrane. It still remains to be shown that the "spherules" are capable of splitting and reproducing.

Some of the world's leading geneticists are doing remarkable work with RNA (ribonucleic acids) and DNA (deoxyribonucleic acids), the two substances that play the basic role in transmitting hereditary traits. DNA is found only in the nuclei of cells, RNA only in the cytoplasm surrounding the cells.

In 1959 Severo Ochoa of New York University and Arthur Kornberg of Stanford University shared the Nobel Prize for physiology and medicine in recognition of their feat in synthesizing each of these basic life substances in the test tube with the aid of a bacterial enzyme. They hope to be able to show that the artificially created substances are biologically active.

OTHER MEDICAL DEVELOPMENTS

How the brain acts as a tape recorder

Dr. Wilder Penfield, head of the Neurological Institute of Montreal, Canada, has demonstrated that individuals can be stimulated to reveal amazingly precise recollections of experiences that occurred more than 20 years earlier.

When a fine electrode is applied to one of the temporal lobes of the brain and a slight electrical current is passed through, the brain reacts with all the exactitude of a tape recorder.

According to Dr. Penfield, "There is hidden away in the brain, a record of the stream of consciousness. It seems to hold the detail of that stream as laid down during each man's waking, conscious hours. Contained in this record are all those things of which the individual was once aware—such details as a man might hope to remember for a few seconds or minutes afterwards, but which are largely lost to voluntary recall after that time.

"This is not memory, as we usually use the word. No man can recall by voluntary effort such a wealth of detail. Many a patient has told me that the experience brought back by the electrode is much more real than remembering."

Dr. Penfield believes that the storehouse of these recollections is located further back in the brain. The temporal lobes, in his opinion, act as transmission belts for sending electrical impulses to the storehouse at the time the original experience takes place. The later electrical stimulation sends a new impulse that revives the earlier experience.

Electrical charges in the brain

Painless electrical charges to the human brain can stimulate feelings of fear, friendliness, or recall of long-forgotten events. Tests have yielded similar results with monkeys, cats and other animals. Dr. Jose M. R. Delgado, Associate Professor of Physiology at the Yale University School of Medicine, who was in charge of the experiments, denies that they "support the distasteful conclusion that motion, emotion and behavior can be directed by electrical forces and that animals and humans can be controlled like robots." Dr. Delgado believes that the electrical current affects already existing patterns but cannot create them.

Other experiments with animals led to remarkable results. Damage to a part of the hypothalamus (a portion of the brain) enormously increased the appetite of rats. Some ate so greedily that their bodies turned into 70 per cent fat. On the other hand, damage to a nearby area of the hypothalamus can result in starvation, even with an abundant food supply available.

Electronic artificial nerve cells

The nervous system of the body is a network of nerve cells that transmit electrical impulses to and from the brain. Despite intensive study, there is still much for scientists to learn about how the nervous system operates.

Research scientists at the Bell Telephone Laboratories have assembled a crude electronic device which ingeniously imitates the workings of the nervous system. Each electronic artificial nerve cell

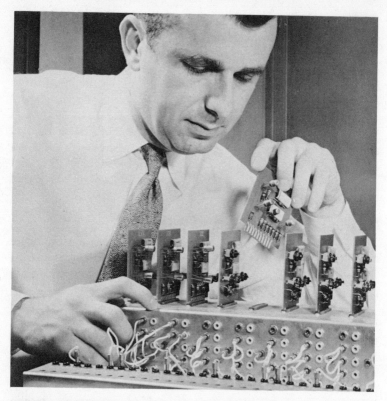

ARTIFICIAL NERVE CELLS: Leon D. Harmon of Bell Telephone Laboratories assembles a network of electronic cells which simulate the functions of nerve cells. Connected in a simple transistorized circuit, these cells imitate some of the functions of nerves in the eye.

is mounted on a three-by-four-inch printed-circuit card. These inexpensive cells are each equipped with four transistors.

Leon D. Harmon, who started the project, pointed out that "the similarities to biological nerves are at best vague and approximate. But by working the problem back and forth between the two disciplines—electronics and physiology—we may learn more about how the nervous system operates."

Like a living nerve cell, the electronic cell delivers a series of electrical pulses when stimulated. Conditions which cause a living cell to fail to respond have the same effect on an electronic cell;

an electronic cell registers "fatigue" by slowing down after it has been stimulated for a long time.

The functions of nerves in the retina of the eye are imitated by equipping the electronic cells with photocells. "On"-receptors, replacing sense organs, pulse when the light increases; "off"-receptors pulse as light decreases; "during"-receptors pulse when the light remains steady. The artificial cells have been adjusted to "see" a continuously flickering light as a steady one—just as the natural eye sees the flickers of motion pictures and television as solid images.

Willem A. Van Bergeijk is working on another model which will imitate the functioning of the ear. By constructing such electronic models, scientists hope to learn more about the way sense organs transmit signals to the brain, which interprets them as the images our eyes see and the sounds our ears hear. They also hope to learn more about the impulses the brain sends out to activate the muscles of arms and legs, eyelids and vocal cords.

A sleep machine

Russian doctors have invented a sleep machine which is used to soothe mental patients, as well as surgical patients who are under local anesthetics.

The machine pulses weak electrical currents into the brain. This suppresses certain wave patterns in the brain, with the result that the patient falls asleep in anywhere from a few seconds to 20 minutes. As long as two electrodes remain fastened to the patient's head, nothing but intense pain will rouse him from sleep.

Pills for the deaf

Almost half the people who are hard of hearing suffer from poor blood circulation in the inner ear, due to constriction of the tiny blood vessels there. This results in hearing losses, buzzing sounds and dizziness.

Dr. Wallace Rubin, a specialist from the Ear, Eye, Nose and Throat Hospital of New Orleans, Louisiana, has found that the drug Arlidin, given by mouth, improves blood circulation with very favorable results. A large number of the patients reported considerable relief from their hearing difficulties; almost all "showed significant improvement."

The juvenile hormone

One of nature's most fascinating mysteries is the way in which a caterpillar "metamorphoses" into a pupa and then into a moth or butterfly. Part of the mystery was stripped away in 1936 when the British zoologist V. B. Wigglesworth of Cambridge University discovered that the process was governed by a hormone (a substance produced by a gland and sent through the body fluids to a specific organ to regulate its activity).

Wigglesworth found that insects in the caterpillar stage produce this "juvenile hormone" (JH) in two tiny glands located in the brain. When the insect is ready for the next stage, the glands stop producing the hormone. In 1956 Professor Carroll M. Williams succeeded in preparing an extract of the hormone, paving the way for some interesting experiments in which he was aided by Dr. Howard A. Schneiderman and Dr. Lawrence I. Gilbert of Cornell University.

In one experiment the scientists discovered that if they deprived a caterpillar of the hormone before it was fully matured, it imme-

BUTTERFLY EMERGING: Wing by wing a butterfly emerges from its chrysalis. The riddle of the caterpillar's transformation into a pupa and then into a butterfly was solved by a British zoologist who discovered that this process is regulated by the "juvenile hormone."

diately turned into a moth. On the other hand, injecting the hormone into a caterpillar made it remain in that stage, without the normal metamorphosis taking place. Other studies revealed that the same hormone was present in a wide variety of animals.

When the hormone was extracted from a cow and injected into a caterpillar, the experimenters achieved the same results as previously, indicating that the hormone was a key element in the life process. They believe that the hormone is also present in human tissues, concentrated mostly in the thymus gland, which is located in the thorax, near the base of the neck. As human beings grow older, this gland shrivels. It may be that the hormone functions in humans in the same way as in animals.

Dr. Williams has suggested two exciting possibilities. "The day is not too far distant," he says, "when we will be able to treat senescence (aging) as we know how to treat pneumonia." Secondly, he foresees a "truly perfect" insecticide which would root out unwanted species, while at the same time man could prevent the aging process in insects which are useful to him.

Radio waves for medical treatment

For more than two decades Dr. A. J. Ginsberg of New York has had a theory that in diathermy (applying heat by means of high-frequency radio waves) something more than heat affects body tissues. What that "something" is remains a mystery, but authorities in the field have a tentative theory that the diathermy treatments stimulate the body's healing apparatus to operate more effectively.

The technique of interrupted heat-therapy involves focusing a powerful radio wave on the affected area for 60 millionths of a second, and then repeating the process 400 to 600 times a second for five to ten minutes. The application of heat to the exposed tissue is short enough, and the pauses long enough, to prevent any raising of temperature in the region affected. The treatment has brought about improvement in patients suffering from rheumatism, sinusitis, boils, sciatica, intestinal spasms, and other ailments.

Virus of trachoma discovered

Trachoma is the greatest single cause of blindness in the world. It is a contagious disease that afflicts 400,000,000 people. Causing itching and burning in the eyelids, it affects vision and often leads to blindness. Since trachoma is contagious, investigators suspected for a long time that it was caused by a germ.

After 50 years of research, the cause of trachoma has definitely been established as a large virus. An English research group, headed by Dr. Leslie H. Collier, grew the virus in eggs and then gave the disease to two blind volunteers—"the first authenticated demonstration of human trachoma induced by a virus cultivated in a laboratory."

Though drugs are useless against most viruses, it is possible to treat some of the larger ones successfully. This is the case with the trachoma virus: sulfadiazine, taken by mouth, cures the infection. Nevertheless, the British research group hopes to develop a vaccine against trachoma.

Safeguarding the food supply

Foot and mouth disease strikes cloven-footed animals, particularly cattle. It is highly contagious, but does not affect human beings. The disease forms painful blisters on the tongue, the inside of the mouth and on the feet. The unfortunate animals, unable to eat, starve to death or else are put to death to end their sufferings.

According to the United States Department of Agriculture, the onset of foot and mouth disease in this country could result in the loss of one quarter of the nation's production of meat, milk and other animal products. One of the department's most important tasks is to keep a vigilant eye out for possible outbreaks of the disease.

But prevention is much more to the point, and the department's animal disease research center has taken the first big step by succeeding in isolating and identifying the virus that causes foot and mouth disease. One-millionth of an inch in diameter, the microorganism was successfully photographed with the aid of the electron microscope. This achievement opens the way for further research to protect cattle against the hitherto deadly virus.

A new surgical mask

Because doctors and nurses are constantly exposed to Staphylococcus germs (page 93), they are likely to be carriers of these microorganisms. Rigorous tests have shown that the conventional gauze facial mask used in surgery allowed an average of 145 bacterial colonies to filter through the mask in a five-minute breathing period.

In order to cut down the danger of infection drastically, Dr. Claude R. Hitchcock and Dr. Joseph Kiser of Minneapolis General Hospital designed a flexible, inexpensive mask made of polyvinyl plastic. The important feature of the mask is a disposable cotton-and-cellulose filter which traps the surgeon's breath, dries and filters it and then forces it to be exhaled backward through the wings of the mask. The average number of bacterial colonies that gets through the new plastic mask is thereby reduced to 1.2 in a five-minute period —an enormous reduction in the danger of infecting the surgical wound.

Mending broken bones

Plaster casts, the standard method for knitting together broken bones, are slow and cumbersome. Dr. Michael P. Mandarino of the Hahnemann Medical College of Philadelphia and Dr. Joseph E. Salvatore of Walter Reed Medical Center devoted four years to perfecting a plastic "glue" that would mend broken bones more rapidly and just as effectively.

Eventually they found a substance that foams and then solidifies on being poured into the hollow channels of broken or diseased bones, and soon hardens in the bone marrow. It has proved 94 per cent successful in the treatment of 250 cases. An important feature of the glue is that bone cells can grow in it. There seem to be no toxic effects or unfavorable reactions from the foreign matter that becomes part of the bone.

The "mechanical cow"

One of the most ingenious scientific developments of our time is the "mechanical cow" now being tested at the British Agricultural Research Council's experimental station near London. The job of this mechanical creature is to extract protein from vegetation, chiefly grass and leaves.

There is a twofold reason for this project. In most parts of the world, human beings do not get an adequate supply of protein. Secondly, most protein is derived from the meat of animals that have previously obtained it from vegetation. In effect, then, the cow is a mechanism for converting the protein content of grass into milk and beef.

But investigation shows that this is an extremely wasteful procedure, with something like 95 per cent of the original protein being lost in the process. This is a life-and-death problem in underdeveloped countries, where few people get all the protein they need. The "mechanical cow" may some day help them get a more nourishing diet.

Here is how the mechanical cow works. Grass or some other vegetation is placed in an elevator and fed into the top of the machine. After undergoing chopping, the grass enters a press which squeezes all the juice out of it. The juice, which contains a large proportion of protein and very little cellulose, is then treated with steam. This forces the protein to sink to the bottom. It is then possible to filter out the protein, which is made into cake-like forms that are convenient to handle.

This process extracts half the protein that was originally in the grass. (Incidentally, the residue of the juice makes good animal fodder.) The extracted protein goes to another experimental center, where it is fed to pigs, for these animals have a digestive system similar to man's. The earliest observations indicate that the animals have flourished on the enriched diet, but it is still too soon to arrive at any definite conclusions.

Sound and Light

ULTRASONICS

Ultrasonics deals with the properties of sound waves that have too high a frequency to be detected by the human ear. Each sound wave has an alternating high and low pressure which together make up a vibration. The number of times such a vibration or "cycle" occurs in a second is called its "frequency." Low-frequency ("bass") sounds have comparatively few vibrations per second; high-frequency ("treble") sounds have a great many vibrations per second.

All motions produce sound waves, but not all these sounds are audible. At both ends of the scale there is a limit to the number of vibrations that can produce audible sounds. We cannot hear sounds that have less than 16 vibrations per second or more than about 17,000 vibrations per second. For example, if you move your hand back and forth, you are producing vibrations in the air; but you cannot hear any sound because fewer than 16 vibrations per second are being produced. On the other end of the scale is the familiar example of the whistle that produces a sound of such high frequency that the human ear cannot hear it, but a dog's ear, differently attuned, can.

Frequency should not be confused with intensity (loudness), which is measured in decibels. It is possible to be painfully disturbed by sounds of more than 120 decibels' intensity—without being able to hear them.

High-frequency waves that are inaudible can be put to many valuable uses; ultrasonic waves can create pressures of 75,000 pounds to the square inch—5,000 times greater than atmospheric pressure. They can also create a localized heat of 20,000 degrees Fahrenheit. In order to convert electrical energy into ultrasonic waves, a transducer or a quartz crystal is used.

Uses of ultrasonics

In the manufacture of cosmetics, the use of frequencies of between 35,000 and 50,000 vibrations per second makes it possible to surround particles of water with oil to prepare a cleansing cream; the reverse process makes a vanishing cream.

Vibrations of anywhere from a thousand to a million a second can be applied to break down tough fibers in frozen meat which has been placed in a brine-filled tank. Because it is frozen, the meat retains its shape and natural juices. The process is said to work equally well with meats, fish, fruits or vegetables without affecting the taste or color of the food.

A number of important industrial processes depend on the use of welded metals. But some metals—aluminum is one of them—are difficult to weld by conventional methods. Westinghouse scientists have therefore developed a process of welding metals by ultrasonic means.

In this process, the two pieces of metal that are to be welded together are overlapped and placed between two metal wheels. A transducer vibrates the wheels to cause a kneading action that takes place 20,000 times a second. This breaks up the oxide coating on the surfaces of the metals and causes the molecules to react so that the metal crystals become fused.

The ultrasonic process is superior to conventional methods in that it requires no application of electric current or outside source of heat to the metals; it calls for no preliminary cleaning procedures; it can weld together dissimilar metals with no untoward effects.

It is likely that home washing machines will eventually operate on ultrasonic principles. At present there is an ultrasonic washing machine for cleaning surgical instruments. Such a machine works more rapidly and efficiently than a conventional machine to remove the tiniest specks of dirt, bits of tissue and dried blood.

Ultrasonic methods are also being used to collect soot in factory chimneys to prevent air pollution by carbon and sulphur. Scientists have experimented with attempts to dissipate fog by ultrasonic means, causing the tiny water droplets to accumulate and then fall as water. Not much is known about these experiments because they are classified, but it is believed that the technique is dangerous because of the intensity of the ultrasonic waves.

HIGHEST-PITCH SOUND: The General Electric Research Laboratory has produced ultrasonic waves with a frequency of 25,000 megacycles (25 billion cycles per second). This frequency is almost $2\frac{1}{2}$ million times greater than the highest-pitch sound the human ear can hear. Above, Dr. Edward H. Jacobsen, who performed the remarkable experiment, adjusts the wave guides which direct the microwaves to a quartz crystal kept in the shiny vertical cylinder at temperatures close to absolute zero. These exceptionally high frequencies will probably have their first scientific application in solid-state research.

The use of ultrasonic waves has a great future in medicine, but it cannot become really widespread until scientists have learned a great deal more about the effect of such waves on body tissues and blood circulation.

However, with the development of techniques to concentrate ultrasonic beams into a focus of microscopic narrowness, it has become possible to employ ultrasonic waves for brain operations of the utmost delicacy. Because surgeons can now pinpoint diseased spots without having to harm healthy tissue, they have succeeded in performing some sensational operations once deemed out of the question.

Another medical use which is destined to become much more common is the ultrasonic diagnosing of lumps in the breast and tumors in the brain. The focusing of a narrow ultrasonic beam on the patient's body produces a pattern of echoes that can be converted into electronic signals and shown on a television picture tube. Similar techniques can be used to diagnose otherwise inaccessible parts of the eye or bone structure.

INFRARED RADIATION*

All matter with a temperature above absolute zero (−459.6 degrees Fahrenheit) emits infrared rays. The higher the temperature, the more intense the radiation. Infrared radiation, which travels in electromagnetic waves and is a form of energy, heats up any object which absorbs it.

Infrared waves range in length from .7 of a micron to 300 microns (a micron measures .00003937 of an inch). These waves are invisible, but they can be detected and utilized by devices that measure radiation, such as a radiometer.

Each substance absorbs a uniquely characteristic amount of infrared radiation; this makes it possible for scientists to identify substances by spectrometric analysis of their capacity for absorbing infrared radiation. (A spectrometer is a device for measuring wave lengths of different kinds of radiation.) From this it is theoretically only a step further to put infrared radiation to many valuable scientific and industrial uses.

---

*For more detailed information about infrared radiation, see *Rays — Visible and Invisible,* by Fred Reinfeld (Sterling Publishing Co., Inc.).

HEAT-SEEKING MISSILES: This U.S. Navy jet-engined combat plane carries two highly effective Sidewinder missiles which operate on infrared principles. The lettering on the tail indicates that the plane is stationed at the U.S. Naval Ordnance Test Station at China Lake, California.

Military infrared uses

The top-secret Midas research program deals with infrared devices that can detect the white-hot warhead of an oncoming ballistic missile. The research scientists hope to refine infrared detection to the point of spotting a missile shortly after it leaves its launching pad, a thousand miles (and more) away. Infrared missile-trackers are already in use at Cape Canaveral, Florida, and on ships and islands in the vicinity.

Whereas radar can be jammed because it depends on the energy transmitted by its own beams, infrared detectors cannot be put out of commission in the same way because they passively pick up the radiation from enemy objects. And the fact that infrared units do not require a transmitter also means an enormous economy in installation and maintenance as compared to radar.

The faster objects move, the hotter they get. This puts radar at a disadvantage, as increased heat blurs the image on the oscilloscope. With infrared detection the reverse is true, as faster motion and increased heat increase the amount of infrared radiation received, making reception stronger and clearer.

The United States has two combat planes on which infrared radiation is used for offense. These are the Sidewinder (Navy) and the Falcon (Air Force), both highly effective against jet aircraft. In the case of the Sidewinder, a lens mechanism "senses" the presence of hot objects such as a jet plane's engine or exhaust. The device gives notice electronically of its discovery, alerting the pilot to release a heat-seeking missile. The result is usually deadly, for even if its prey twists and turns, the missile will do the same, keeping after its quarry until it destroys it.

Scientists are now directing their research toward an important improvement in infrared devices—measuring distance by relating it to the intensity of the radiation detected. Even more basic—and more difficult—is the research on an infrared detection and guidance system capable of hunting and destroying an enemy supersonic missile while it is still far from its target.

FUNCTIONAL EQUIPMENT: This pilot is wearing a specially designed pressurized suit intended for high-altitude flight. (Note the knee "pocket" for instructions and memoranda.) At right, the Sidewinder missile, which is equally effective at low and high altitudes.

Industrial infrared uses

A potential use for infrared radiation which at present seems visionary is infrared automation of chemical and glassmaking plants. As the manufacturing processes depend on heat, it is conceivable that automatic devices could give a comparatively small working force the necessary directions for operating the machinery.

Today infrared heating units are being used for a variety of specialized tasks. A cold-storage warehouse, for example, uses infrared heating to keep employees warm as they work on a food-conveyor belt. Another warehouse uses infrared heating to prevent shipments of liquids from freezing when they are unloaded in cold weather. Similar units are used to warm swimming pools.

Some chemical firms use infrared spectrometers for identifying drugs in bottles and containers to make sure they are properly labelled. High-speed presses are kept at the right speed by means of infrared radiometers. Such presses also use heat units which dry the printed pages to keep them from smearing as they come off the press. However, if the temperature is too high the paper will scorch. The radiometer maintains a steady check on the temperature to avoid spoilage.

Infrared testing is valuable in many industrial research projects. In a research laboratory, for example, chemists wanted to find out where and at what temperature a tire would blow out. They used a radiometer to detect heat changes by focusing the instrument on the outside of a tire that was whirled around a simulated roadbed. Using an alarm system and a recorder, the scientists located the site of the most likely damage. This gave them the information they needed to fortify the tire and make it more durable.

Space

SATELLITES

The outbreak of a war has always stimulated efforts to gain a military advantage by the invention of weapons more powerful than any the enemy possesses. Then, when the war is over, the basic principle of a new weapon is applied to peacetime uses. This technological process was particularly noticeable during and after World War II, the most scientific of all wars.

In the closing phase of the war the Germans succeeded in launching their dreaded "buzz-bombs"—missiles with explosive warheads which were given their initial impetus by rockets, and then guided electronically to a general target. The peacetime application of these techniques ushered in the age of space exploration when scientists adapted them to launch instrument-bearing earth satellites at speeds great enough—over 18,000 miles per hour—to keep them in orbit around the earth, but not great enough to enable them to escape from the earth's gravitational pull and disappear into the solar system.

That is why the Russians named their first successful satellite *Sputnik zemli* ("companion of the earth"). This satellite, the first ever launched by man into space, lasted from October 4, 1957 until January 4, 1958. Circling the earth at a distance of 150 miles, Sputnik I took 96 minutes for a complete circuit. At this height there is still enough air left to cause friction—resistance to motion. Slowly the satellite's orbit was changed as it spiraled down gradually. Eventually air density became so great that enough friction was generated to consume the satellite in the same way that meteors are destroyed.

The launching of the satellites has opened up a whole new field of scientific exploration. Hurtling into space, they have sent back much valuable new information about the composition of the atmosphere and conditions in space: temperature, electrical conditions, nature and location of radiation belts, strength of the earth's magnetic field. And, as we shall see, scientists have various ways of applying this information to problems relating to manned space travel, more accurate weather prediction and improved radio and television transmitting.

Vanguard satellites

These comparatively small satellites may be taken as typical of the design and function of satellites in general. The Vanguard type is a hollow sphere with a diameter of 20 inches. Made of magnesium only 3/100ths of an inch thick, it is gold plated on its outer side and covered with a bright mirror-like aluminum coating. It has 4 antennas, each about 24 inches long, for its radio transmitters. While the satellite is still in the rocket, the antennas remain folded back, but once the satellite is launched, the antennas spring into working position.

Each satellite is used for specialized scientific purposes and the instrumentation varies accordingly. The weight of one of these satellites is upwards of 20 pounds, depending on the instruments carried aloft. The small size of these satellites, determined by the nature and strength of the launching techniques, in turn calls for a great deal of ingenuity and miniaturization of the instruments used. Some of these weigh just a few ounces and are more delicate than a watch.

Each satellite contains an electronic brain and a magnetic memory. Its radio equipment operates as long as its batteries are able to function. The tiny radio transmitter ("Minitrack") weighs 13 ounces but has a broadcasting range of 4,000 miles. The function of the magnetic-memory unit is to store the data collected by the instruments. The information is played back to the transmitter, which sends out varying signals which are picked up on earth by tracking stations. These stations tape the signals received.

By employing the appropriate electronic techniques it is possible to convert signals into visible patterns of jagged lines on film. Scientists who study these patterns can interpret the conditions recorded by the satellite's instruments.

Taking temperature readings presents a problem, as a conventional thermometer could never survive the extremes of fierce heat of the sun in daytime and the intense cold of outer space at night. The solution is a "thermistor," a small metal disk fastened to the outside of the satellite. The passage of an electrical current through the disk results in variations in the electrical resistance of the disk as the temperature goes up or down; this in turn modifies the strength of the current accordingly. These changes are stored in the memory unit and then transmitted to the tracking stations.

Billions of meteors, varying in size from dust particles to much larger masses, penetrate into the earth's atmosphere daily. The satellite contains three instruments to provide information about meteor showers.

One of these instruments is an erosion gauge, also mounted outside. It is nothing more than a tiny metal ribbon with an electrical connection. The impact of the meteors wears down the ribbon, and the strength of the current declines proportionately. The measurement of the decrease is transmitted to the tracking stations.

SPACE EXPLORER: This Vanguard satellite is being prepared for launching. It contains instruments for recording data about the earth's magnetic field, solar X-rays and space environmental conditions.

ZERO PLUS SPLIT SECONDS: Vanguard II, carried in the third stage of a rocket, rises from the launching site on February 17, 1959. Orbiting the earth every 126 minutes, its job was to relay data on the earth's cloud cover to tracking stations. The satellite is expected to remain aloft for decades, possibly for centuries.

The second instrument is a microphone inside the satellite which records the sound of meteors striking the satellite. The third, also inside, is a pressure gauge which records any piercing of the shell of the satellite by a meteor big enough and heavy enough to do the job.

Other satellites

In December 1959 no less than nine satellites were circling the earth. One was the Russian Sputnik III. All the others were American: three Vanguards, two Discoverers, three Explorers. In addition, it was believed that two satellites were orbiting around the sun—the American Pioneer IV, and the Russian Lunik I (Mechta).

The most useful of these was perhaps Explorer VI, the "paddle-wheel" satellite launched in August 1959. Its instruments transmitted valuable information about the Van Allen radiation belts (see page 128) and also took some mediocre television pictures of the earth and its cloud cover at heights of up to 26,000 miles. The launching of Explorer VI was to test the feasibility of capturing energy from the sun to send messages across millions of miles.

Lunik I, launched in January 1959, was the first object to attain a velocity sufficient to enable it to escape the earth's magnetic field. ("Escape velocity" is 7 miles a second—25,000 miles per hour.) It became the first artificial planet to orbit around the sun and while its batteries held out it sent back information about the magnetic field of the earth and the moon, the gas components of interplanetary matter, meteoric particles and cosmic radiation.

Vanguard II, launched on February 17, 1959, is expected to remain aloft for decades, possibly for centuries. As the first "weather eye," it was designed to survey the cloud cover over the sunlit portions of the earth. Vanguard II was a pioneering attempt to demonstrate that such observations from space were perfectly feasible.

Pioneer IV was the first American artificial planet to go into orbit around the sun. Launched on March 3, 1959, it weighed only 13½ pounds as compared to the 800-pound Lunik I that the Russians had orbited around the sun two months earlier. The signals from its transmitter came in so sharply that the Jodrell Bank Observatory in England could have picked them up at a distance of 4,000,000 miles. After three days and 400,000 miles out, the transmitter went dead, but the satellite will continue to circle around the sun indefinitely.

THE MOON

What the moon is like

Astronomers believe that the moon was formed at the same time as the earth, perhaps $5\frac{1}{2}$ billion years ago. Originally the moon was about 20,000 miles away from the earth, with a lot of smaller satellites beyond it. When the oceans were formed on the earth, the gravitational pull of the moon caused the action of the tides, which slowed down the rotation of the earth on its axis. (According to the astronomers, this slowing-down process is still going on at the rate of 1 second every 100,000 years.) This in turn made the moon spiral outward, so that the distance between moon and earth became much greater. This distance varies, the average distance being 238,857 miles and the shortest distance 221,463 miles.

As the moon moved away—so the astronomers theorize—it crashed into some of the smaller satellites, and the impacts created the numerous pits and craters which are visible on the moon's surface. Some 30,000 of these have been detected on the bleak surface of the moon. There are a dozen or so rugged mountain ranges, some of them with peaks higher than any on the earth.

There is no water on the moon, and its "seas" are really extinct lava fields pocked with tension cracks and compression ridges and probably covered with dust. No erosion has taken place on the moon, as it has little or no atmosphere and no air. For the same reason there is no sound on the moon and, as far as we know, no life.

The earth is four times the size of the moon and weighs 81 times more. Consequently gravity is much weaker on the moon, and it has been calculated that a man on its surface could jump up 20 or 30 feet.

While we speak of the moon revolving around the earth, it would be more precise to say that they both spin about a mutual center of gravity located inside the earth. The earth rotates on its tilted axis a little over 27 times for every single complete revolution around the mutual center of gravity. The moon's rotation on its axis takes about the same amount of time as its spin about the common center of gravity; consequently we always see the same side of the moon, and up to the time the Russians released the pictures taken by Lunik III, no one had ever seen the far side of the moon which is always turned away from us.

A "day" on the moon lasts two of our weeks. Because of the lack of shielding atmosphere, the climate runs to harsh extremes ranging from 250 degrees above zero at "noon" to 215 degrees below zero at "midnight."

Reaching the moon

The landing of a rocket on the moon is one of the great historic steps in the development of a manned exploration of the solar system.

Whereas Lunik I was the first rocket to escape from the earth's magnetic field, Lunik II, launched on September 12, 1959, repeated this feat and in addition was the first rocket to reach the surface of the moon. This occurred on September 14 after the rocket had travelled 230,000 miles in 35 hours. The deviation from the velocity required for leaving the earth was calculated as no more than 1/10 of 1 per cent. This is the most accurate firing of a rocket that has ever taken place. The rocket together with its instruments weighed 858 pounds, much more than any satellite so far launched by American scientists.

The flight was timed to take place in that part of the month when the rocket's path would be most nearly parallel with the earth's surface. The purpose of this was to reduce to the minimum the force of gravity on the rocket as it left the earth. A special mechanism released a sodium cloud from the rocket when it went into orbit, in order to make it easier for observers to trace its journey. Before its departure the rocket was sterilized to avoid the possibility of contaminating the moon with harmful microorganisms that flourish on our planet.

Soviet scientists announced that the rocket was equipped with a variety of instruments to enable them to study "the magnetic pole of the earth and the magnetic poles of the moon, the radiation around the earth, the intensity and variation of cosmic radiation, the gas components of interplanetary substance and meteor particles." The rocket carried two transmitters for sending back the gathered data.

Although some authorities believe the moon has a very feeble magnetic field, the rocket could detect no evidence at all to support this view. This was of special interest to scientists who believe that the earth's magnetic field is caused by the rotation of its liquid core

GIANT SATELLITE: While this 100-foot-diameter satellite is on the ground, it requires no less than 40,000 pounds of air to inflate the huge sphere. In orbit, on the other hand, a few pounds of gas would do the trick. It is made of an ultra-thin plastic film coated for extra strength with a film of aluminum. The lack of a rigid skin will be no disadvantage in the high altitudes where this satellite will orbit. To cope with the problems of meteorite puncture or skin permeability, the satellite will have a replacement gas system dependent on an evaporating liquid or a suitable type of crystals.

This satellite is expected to be useful in two ways: to reflect radio and radar signals for long-distance communication (see page 182), and also to be used for a flight to the moon.

As a satellite, it might go into orbit at an altitude of between 800 and 1000 miles, lasting perhaps two months at most. As a lunar probe, the instrumentation it carries would give its exact position at all times.

The chief advantage of the flexible skin is that this satellite can be folded into a metal container with a 30-inch diameter in a rocket, automatically inflating when released in space by the rocket. The satellite comes in different weights; one type weighs 190 pounds, including the metal container.

of molten iron. In their opinion, this rotation, like the functioning of a dynamo, creates the magnetic field.

Another related theory holds that the moon is solid all through, lacking a similar liquid core. If the explanation of the earth's magnetic field is correct, then the absence of a lunar magnetic field and of a liquid core would seem to bear out the theory about the earth's magnetism.

The rocket also found no evidence of radiation belts around the moon. These two negative findings are consistent with each other, since a radiation belt (such as the Van Allen radiation belts around the earth) is made up of radiation trapped by a powerful magnetic field.

The far side of the moon

After centuries of speculation, man had his first sight of the far side of the moon when the pictures taken by Lunik III were released. This was the 613-pound rocket launched by Soviet scientists on October 3, 1959. The photographs taken with the equipment on Lunik III have been pronounced "the most impressive feat of the space age since the launching of the first Sputnik."

Timing was all-important, for the flight had to be scheduled for a time when the new moon was seen on earth. This would mean that the far side of the moon was getting the most brilliant sunlight it received during the month, assuring favorable conditions for taking pictures. It took hairline accuracy to plan the flight so that Lunik would be in the best position at the time of the photographing.

Until the time for the picture-taking, the rocket had been held to a spinning motion in order to distribute the sun's heat evenly and to keep the instruments in good condition. Then an electronic signal from the earth stopped the spinning motion in order to give the cameras a steady focus. A "sensor" device (probably a photo-electric cell) swung the camera lenses on their target. Both instruments—a close-up camera and a panoramic camera—were equipped with automatic film-developing devices.

For 40 minutes the cameras took photos which were developed directly on the film drum. The instruments in Lunik III contained radiophoto scanners similar to the facsimile system used for telephoto pictures. As the photocell scanned the developed picture line by line, it emitted an electrical impulse proportional to the intensity of the white, gray and dark spots in the picture. For 12 hours at a time, when Lunik was in line-of-sight with the receiving stations on the earth, its signals were transmitted to them—almost 300,000 miles away.

The Russians claim that the transmitted images have a much finer definition than ordinary television pictures and wirephotos used by the press services. The first Lunik picture of the far side of the moon seems to bear out the theory that the hitherto unseen side of the moon is much smoother than the familiar side that is visible to us. The picture showed a landscape that was monotonous and surprisingly lacking in outstanding features.

It has been pointed out that the brilliant sunlight prevailing at the time the photographs were taken blotted out a certain amount of significant detail. However, Professor Aleksandr A. Mikhailov, a leading Russian astronomer, believes that the difference in the appearance of the two sides probably goes back to the conditions which governed the formation of the moon.

Travelling to the moon

According to Babylonian legend, 5,000 years ago a shepherd named Etana wanted to fly on an eagle to the moon to complain to the gods about high taxes. From the 17th century on, many fantasies about travel to the moon have appeared. Cyrano de Bergerac was the first to think of getting to the moon by means of rocket propulsion.

But these charming fantasies have given way to serious study of the problems involved in getting to the moon, a feat which most scientists expect to see accomplished by 1970. After that it may take another 10 years, they speculate, to establish bases on the moon and make it possible to live there.

The difficulties of human existence on the moon would be formidable. Because of the lack of atmosphere the explorers would need a dwelling that was protected from the sun's radiation, from severe cold and from the impact of meteorites. They would be likely to make their home in a transparent dome-shaped structure, raising their food in gardens that would have the added value of turning back some of their carbon dioxide into oxygen.

The colonists would use nuclear power or sunlight to generate electricity. They might even turn the craters into dwellings by roofing them over. But before they set up housekeeping on the moon, a very baffling problem must be solved—how to prepare for a safe landing by slowing down from the tremendous speeds at which spaceships will have to travel.

RADIATION IN SPACE

Project Argus

In the fall of 1958 United States Navy personnel and scientists carried out what has been described as "the greatest scientific experiment of all time." Although thousands of people were involved in the project, it was not publicly revealed until almost seven months later. The military aspects of Project Argus remain shrouded in secrecy.

The project arose from the desire on the part of scientists to study the effects of the earth's magnetism in space. The earth acts as a giant magnet, creating lines of force that cause compass needles to point to the magnetic north and south poles. These lines of force reach out beyond the atmosphere into space. What happens when charged particles, such as electrons and protons come in contact with the earth's magnetic field? This was the basic question that Project Argus was designed to answer.

Nicholas Constantine Christofilos, an atomic scientist with highly original ideas, formulated a theory that the charged particles would be trapped by the earth's magnetic field and would whirl about in complicated spiral paths. The discovery of the Van Allen radiation belts indicated that this is what actually happens. The question was whether man could produce enough electrons to create a world-wide effect, or whether these electrons would be "a teaspoonful in a sea of natural radiation."

The most efficient source of such artificially created radiation is a nuclear explosion. Three atom bombs, exploded 300 miles above the earth after being sent aloft by 5-stage and 6-stage missiles from the "Norton Sound," a U.S. Navy missile ship, were used as a basis for the experiment. When such a bomb is exploded in space and huge quantities of electrons are released, there is no counterpressure in the vacuum to prevent indefinite expansion of the "fireball." In

A SPACE-ROCKET VIEW OF EARTH: This remarkable photograph of the earth was taken at an altitude of 200 miles by a movie camera placed in the recoverable capsule in the nose cone of an Atlas intercontinental ballistic missile. The picture, which reveals a linear distance of 2,000 miles of the earth's surface, was taken at the point where the main stage of the missile was falling away after separation from the nose cone.

about an hour's time the earth was covered with a thin curtain of radiation resulting from the explosion.

As predicted, the released electrons were trapped by the lines of the earth's magnetic field. Artificial auroras were created. Magnetic storms were set off, with resulting disturbances in radio and radar reception. Only electrons that have more than a million electron volts of energy, moving at almost the speed of light, were trapped by the magnetic field. The auroras were caused by the collision of these electrons with atoms.

The military significance of the test can only be guessed at. One speculation was that since nuclear explosions in space can cause disruption of electronic warning systems, they might be used by an enemy to put these systems out of commission during an air attack.

Another theory is that such explosions might be used defensively to release enough neutrons to detonate enemy missiles or render them inactive. On the other hand, missile warheads could be shielded with some neutron-absorbing material such as boron 10.

The radiation set off by the nuclear explosions took about four months to dissipate. Because of the comparatively small size of the bombs and the distance of the explosions from the earth, the scientists who supervised the test were confident that none of the resulting radiation reached the earth.

The Van Allen radiation belts

Launched on December 6, 1958, the Pioneer III rocket brought back definite information about the existence of two high-radiation belts that girdle the earth. The radiation counters of the rocket (which rose to a height of 63,000 miles), reported the existence of two distinct radiation belts having a doughnut shape.

The inner belt extends from 1,400 to 3,400 miles above the surface of the earth. Then there is a marked decrease in radiation, with a second belt of intense radiation extending from 8,000 to 12,000 miles above the surface.

At the center of each belt the radiation is so powerful that 45 hours of exposure to it would prove fatal. Spaceships would therefore have to have enough shielding to protect their crews. It is believed that these belts center above the equator. If this proves correct, the safest routes for spaceships would be over the poles, where the radiation would be weakest or nonexistent.

The radiation belts are made up of electrons and protons shot out from the sun and trapped by the earth's magnetic field. Dr. Fred Singer of the University of Maryland has suggested that the inner radiation belt could be rendered safe by firing a satellite of heavy metal into it.

With the electrified particles moving at almost the speed of light, the mathematical chances of their hitting the satellite and being greatly slowed down would be very high. This would result in their leaving the radiation belt, so that in a few years at most the radiation belt would be "swept" clear of them. According to Dr. Singer's calculations, it might take a century for the belt to build up to its present radiation intensity.

PROBLEMS AND PROSPECTS OF THE SPACE AGE

Columbus's unwitting discovery of the New World changed the course of history. Yet it has been completely dwarfed by the exploration of space which started with the successful orbiting of the first artificial satellite on October 4, 1957. The prospectives of further discovery and exploration are as extensive as the universe itself. And, because the problems and complications are without precedent, they have some baffling features.

For example, satellites use radio frequencies which are also used on earth. In time we may have several hundred satellites hurtling through space, all using frequencies already bespoken, and possibly affecting radio reception—unless a timely international agreement sets aside specific channels for the satellites. Another problem is the possibility of damage caused by mechanical failure of a satellite.

Even more complicated is the problem of developing a universally recognized system of Space Law. As Andrew Haley of the American Rocket Society puts it:

"Initially, space vehicles will be owned by nations or groups of nations and extension of international regulation will be fought jealously. But gradually and inexorably traffic will increase, new propulsive systems will be found which will reduce the cost of construction and operation, commercial enterprise will demand access to space, emigration will commence, meteorite mining will become an industrial objective, and all the ancient problems of law will be reasserted under vastly more complicated circumstances."

Today, outer space is a No Man's Land which belongs to everybody and nobody; no one can say whether there will eventually be an agreement making space, like the high seas, available to all, or whether it will be partitioned into zones.

On the other hand, some of the possibilities of space research are definitely hopeful. There are experts who believe, for example, that by 1970 it will be possible to travel from one spot on earth to another in planes that will fly 10 times (or more) the speed of sound. In these "hypersonic" planes a trip from New York to California will take a half-hour, while a New York-Moscow flight should take no more than two hours.

Even more fanciful is the concept of an "Orbital Post Office" which will transmit mail across the oceans in a satellite. In 1957, 428,000,000 letters were sent across the Atlantic. The Orbital Post Office would transmit an even larger volume of mail without sending a single letter.

This is how the post office would work. Electronic transmitting stations would be set up in the United States and Europe. Letters would be written on standardized forms, opened in the post office and electronically "scanned," converted into an electronic code, which would be sent off in one or more satellites and then transcribed to paper at the receiving end. Such a system should become feasible in the 1960's, but whether potential users would reconcile themselves to a standard form and the absence of privacy is a question that cannot readily be answered in advance.

There are two fields in which space research should pay tangible dividends in a fairly short time. By 1962 it should be possible to set up the first experimental television relay stations in space (see page 181). Later on, several more such satellite stations, 22,300 miles above the earth, will make it possible for telecasts to be received anywhere on earth from any other spot on the globe. The method will be cheap and effective.

These new facilities will become available just in the nick of time. In 1960 the number of cable and radio messages was estimated to reach 3 million. By 1970 that number is expected to have increased sevenfold. For several years there has been an increasingly strenuous struggle for radio and television channels. (The competition has become so keen that in 1959 radio astronomers narrowly missed being deprived of almost all the channels available to them; had this happened, a highly promising branch of science would have been virtually wiped out.) The use of orbiting satellites will therefore come just in time to relieve the pressure.

Satellites have already been used experimentally to pick up electronic signals and rebroadcast them. In the next few years, satellites will gradually take on more and more complicated functions. One type of satellite, for example, fully equipped with its own transmitters, receivers, control devices and solar power, will be able to carry 250 individual conversations at the same time—as compared to 44, the maximum possible on a cable.

The other field which promises rapid progress is weather forecasting (see page 189). Satellites will enable scientists to predict coming weather as much as two months ahead. According to the United States Weather Bureau, "Meteorological satellites should make possible the immediate detection of new storm formations—hurricanes, extratropical cyclones, etc.—any place over the globe."

In the Arctic, the Southern Hemisphere and over most of the oceans, there is no systematic observation of weather conditions, despite the fact that some of our worst storms originate in these areas. Based on their experience with Vanguard II in February 1959, scientists are confident that satellite weather observation will be a great success.

As these satellites become more efficient and more versatile, they will record essential information about such factors as temperature, atmospheric pressure, cloud density, storm areas and solar radiation anywhere in the world. The analysis of this information will give us weather forecasting far more precise than any we have had up to now.

Theoretical research is certain to make giant strides. The National Aeronautics and Space Administration is planning a series of telescope satellites. The 200-inch telescope at Mount Palomar has a range of 4 billion light-years. A telescope half as large, placed in a satellite orbiting 500 miles above the earth, would increase this range considerably—perhaps even double it. The resulting additions to astronomical knowledge might revolutionize our basic conceptions about the nature of the universe.

RADIO ASTRONOMY

Radio astronomy started accidentally in 1931 when a radio engineer of the Bell Telephone Laboratories detected strange radio noises which he finally traced to outer space. During World War II radio waves from the sun were found to be causing interference in radar reception. Bit by bit the origin of the radio noises was traced to planets and stars.

These radio sources are billions and billions of times more powerful than the transmitters with which we are familiar. Some of them are thought to be the remains of exploding stars, known as novae and supernovae. The most powerful source of energy by far is the awesome constellation Cygnus, which is 270,000,000 light years away. (A light-year is equivalent to a distance of 6,000,000,000,000 miles.) It "broadcasts" with an energy of 1,000 billion billion billion megawatts (1 followed by 30 zeros). A conventional radio transmitter of 1 megawatt (1,000 kilowatts) is considered very powerful by our standards.

Radio telescope research indicates that the constellation Cygnus originated in a "collision" (or meshing) of two galaxies travelling through space, each made up of billions of stars.

This new form of astronomy has also provided radio reception from the great hydrogen clouds in outer space, and has offered evidence that these huge clouds may be the ever-continuing source of new stars and galaxies.

Radio astronomers feel that by constructing larger and larger radio telescopes they may be able to arrive at the answers to such questions as: How large is the universe? Has it had a beginning? Will it have an end? How has it evolved?

The largest radio telescope

The United States is building the world's greatest radio telescope at Sugar Grove, West Virginia, about 40 miles away from the National Radio Astronomy Observatory at Green Bank in the same state. This telescope will have a diameter of 600 feet, a considerable increase over both the telescope at Jodrell Bank in England (250 feet) and a Soviet radio telescope with a diameter of 350 feet.

The radio telescope at Sugar Grove is expected to "look" out into

SPACE SENTINEL: The 50-foot-diameter radio telescope at the Naval Research Laboratory will continue to be a valuable research tool even though it will be dwarfed by such spectacularly large radio telescopes as the one under construction at Sugar Grove, West Virginia.

space for a distance of 38 billion light years, or 228,000,000 billion billion (228 followed by 21 zeros) miles. This range is 19 times greater than that of the Mount Palomar telescope, which probes immeasurably farther than any other optical telescope. The far-seeing radio telescope, which will be known as the Naval Radio-Research Station, should cost about $80,000,000.

Since no one knows the size of the universe, the range of the new telescope may actually exceed the universe's size. Some astronomers, in fact, believe that the limit of the observable universe does not exceed 10 billion light years. The point is that galaxies receding from the earth move at an increasingly rapid rate as they recede. Once the speed of recession reaches the speed of light (at a distance of 10 billion light years), the light of these galaxies can never reach the earth; for, as Einstein demonstrated, the speed of light is the absolute limit of speed in our universe. (Radio waves, being electromagnetic in character, travel at the same speed as light.)

Shifts in radio signals are expected to measure the velocity at which the universe is expanding. It should also be possible to determine the density of the galaxies. It would then become feasible to find out whether the universe is flat or curved, finite or infinite. If it ever should become possible to send rockets to Saturn, the most distant planet (745,000,000 miles away), the great radio telescope would be able to pick up signals from the rocket. In addition, scientists expect to use the telescope for secret military work and space communications.

The functioning of the giant telescope will involve technical problems of fantastic complexity. This structure, made up of 20,000 tons of steel and aluminum, can work properly only if the alignment of its parts is maintained to within a fraction of an inch. However, it will be subjected to tremendous distortion stress from rotation and from the action of the elements. To counteract these pressures, the engineers have designed ingenious servomechanisms (automatic devices operated by remote control) that will automatically keep the sections in alignment no matter what powerful forces they are subjected to.

The parabolic "dish" and antenna will be mounted on a huge "ferris wheel" capable of rotating nearly 180 degrees. The wheel structure itself will turn on enormous rollers mounted on a circular track on the ground. It will take millions of watts of energy to manipulate this imposing structure. An inertial guidance system (see page 36) will point the telescope in the desired direction.

A radio "eye" looks at a galaxy

The National Radio Astronomy Observatory at Green Bank, West Virginia, has a dish-shaped antenna with a diameter of 85 feet. Using this equipment, astronomers have received radio signals from the Milky Way and have sought to map it on the basis of intensity of the signals received.

The radio spectrum of the galaxy shows two center regions that are "hot"—indicating that they may be twin clusters of stars. The outer regions are cooler, and seem to take the form of a ring surrounding the center of the galaxy.

The distance of the center of the galaxy from the earth is 25,000 light-years. If the twin sources of the radio signals turn out to be masses of stars, they may well be equivalent to a billion suns. The inner region is about 40 light-years from the galaxy's center, while the outer regions are about 200 light-years from the center.

With the construction of larger and more efficient radio telescopes, it may become possible to explain the origin of the galaxy and the reason for its spiral formation. This research represents a very considerable advance over what previously could be learned with optical telescopes.

A sky station in space

Scientists of the Raytheon Company have developed what seems like a highly practical plan for establishing unmanned, electronically operated saucer-like platforms many miles from the earth. They anticipate, as a result, important advances in missile detection, long-range communications, navigational and weather-forecasting aids, study of the atmosphere, surveillance, television transmission and other fields.

Installing and maintaining these space platforms will be made possible by an almost miraculous development—the transmission of sizeable quantities of power without the use of wires. The "weightless fuel" comes in the form of high-frequency radio waves in the microwave range.

In ordinary radio transmitting, focusing the signals is out of place,

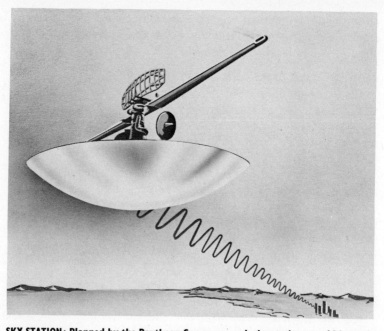

SKY STATION: Planned by the Raytheon Company, such sky stations would hover in fixed positions, miles above the earth. They would be powered by microwave energy beamed from the ground. They could be raised or lowered as desired.

as they are intended to be picked up by many receivers at all points of the compass. But in this case, where the energy is to be beamed at a single target, focusing is essential; the energy would be dissipated if it were sent out in all directions. However, longer wave lengths are impractical because they call for larger antennas to focus the radiation.

On board the platforms, special equipment will convert the beamed energy into heat; in turn, a gas-turbine engine and compressor will convert the heat energy into mechanical energy.

In many electronic fields—electronic computers, for example—design engineers try to reduce the generating of heat to a minimum, as heat can seriously affect operating efficiency. In the case of the sky station, however, an increase in produced heat yields more propulsion power.

UNMANNED YET VERSATILE: Controlled from the ground, the sky stations could serve many functions: they could give warnings of impending attack, make long-range television feasible, help to make air traffic safer.

The platform is to be raised to the desired position and lowered from it with energy supplied by a lightweight supplementary chemical power plant. This plant can also function as a source of emergency power.

Here are some of the intended applications of this revolutionary device:

Detection devices on the platform would greatly increase the efficiency of existing defense networks.

Long-range communications would become vastly more reliable as messages could be beamed from one platform to another, hundreds of miles away. It is estimated that one such skypath link could handle well over 100,000 telegraph messages.

It would require only a few sky stations to make television feasible across the oceans. Conventional telecasting is hampered by the curvature of the earth's surface. The sky stations would operate at altitudes high enough to rule out this factor completely.

The sky stations could also function as remarkably efficient "lighthouses." If such stations were suspended over large cities they could make use of glass bulbs filled in each case with a specific gas giving off a characteristic glow. A jet pilot would be warned that he was approaching a certain city while he was still 450 miles away. Neon, which has a red-orange glow, and xenon, which emits a blue light, are typical examples of the gases which might be used.

The heart of the transmitting system is the Amplitron, a micro-wave amplifier tube two feet tall, with a high efficiency that prevents the dissipation of heat energy. A battery of these tubes generates large amounts of microwave energy which is beamed by a group of 400-foot-square antennas.

As the beams ascend skyward, they converge until they finally focus on a circular area on the platform less than 100 feet in dia-meter. A circular array of antennas of about the same diameter as the focused beam picks up the microwave energy so that it can be converted into heat that enables a stream of compressed air to drive a heat engine. The heat turbines will operate the helicopter-type rotor blades which will enable the platforms to hover in fixed positions.

A radio signal to Venus

Early in 1958 a group of physicists and electrical engineers at Massachusetts Institute of Technology bounced a radio beam off the planet Venus back to earth. The distance travelled by the radio signal was more than a hundred times greater than the earth-to-moon radar signal sent to the moon by the United States Army Signal Corps in 1946. A powerful radio transmitter sent the beams in a predetermined direction. The return signals were received with the aid of a dish-shaped antenna with an 84-foot diameter and a weight of 90 tons.

The radio signals were transmitted on two separate occasions, and it took about a month of work with an electronic computer to sift out the returned signals from stray static in outer space.

On the first attempt Venus was 27,530,000 miles away from the earth. The radio signals, travelling at the speed of light, took almost five minutes for the round trip. Two days later, when Venus was 28,227,000 miles from the earth, the trip was correspondingly longer—a fraction over five minutes.

The object of these experiments was to check the measurement of interplanetary distances. In addition, the scientists hoped to get some idea of the composition of Venus, which is swathed in an impenetrable curtain of clouds. However, they concluded that they will need more sensitive equipment to get the desired information.

THE COMING AGE OF SPACE TRAVEL

Space travel will eventually become feasible, but only after some gruelling problems have been solved. It will not be easy to accustom astronauts to such conditions as these: "dropped" objects do not fall; the absence of frictional force makes it possible for an object to move forever; no air is available for breathing; slowed-down objects move more rapidly, whereas if they are speeded up they move more slowly. The speeds required are almost beyond comprehension—whereas a jet plane travels at 10 miles a minute, a space vehicle must move at 5 miles per *second*.

The distances involved are even more fantastic: at a speed of 26 miles per second, it would take three years to reach Neptune, and almost 30,000 years to arrive at the nearest star. The sun and the orbit of Pluto are separated by a sphere with a 7-billion-mile diameter.

Both the United States and the Soviet Union are planning their moon explorations to proceed along these lines: (1) studying the surface of the moon by means of a satellite circling around the moon; (2) landing instruments on the moon to make chemical findings and report back by radio; (3) placing a small vehicular tank on the surface of the moon to explore it and give scientists a better idea of its properties; (4) sending a man to the moon—1970 seems the likely date.

The positioning of satellite space stations will simplify space travel. A spaceship leaving the earth has to overcome the force of the earth's gravity. An additional difficulty is that a spaceship leaving the earth needs an enormous amount of fuel; in turn this requires greater launching power.

On the other hand, a spaceship departing from a space station would be moving at the rate of 5 miles a second (the speed of the satellite) even before leaving the station. It would only need to accelerate to 7 miles a second to overcome any magnetic pull from the earth.

In some ways the design of a spaceship to the moon is simpler than we might think. For example, since the moon has no atmosphere the spaceship would not require wings. And since the space between the earth and the moon is virtually a vacuum, there would be no need for streamlining the ship.

Even the state of weightlessness is not an insoluble problem. One suggestion is to line the spaceship with steel and have the passengers wear magnetized shoes. An even more ingenious idea is to have the

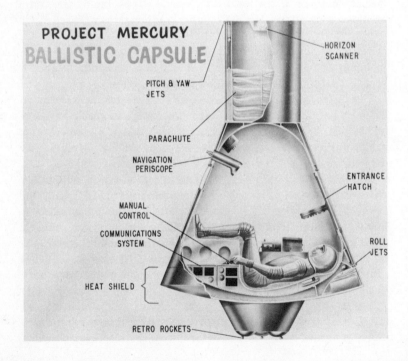

PROJECT MERCURY
BALLISTIC CAPSULE

HORIZON SCANNER

PITCH & YAW JETS

PARACHUTE

NAVIGATION PERISCOPE

MANUAL CONTROL

COMMUNICATIONS SYSTEM

HEAT SHIELD

ENTRANCE HATCH

ROLL JETS

RETRO ROCKETS

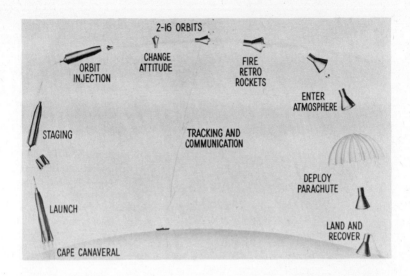

2-16 ORBITS

ORBIT INJECTION

CHANGE ATTITUDE

FIRE RETRO ROCKETS

ENTER ATMOSPHERE

STAGING

TRACKING AND COMMUNICATION

DEPLOY PARACHUTE

LAUNCH

LAND AND RECOVER

CAPE CANAVERAL

PROJECT MERCURY: This is the enormously complicated, long-term project on which American scientists are working to put the first manned space flight into orbit. (Above) A greatly simplified plan of the contemplated flight trajectory. (Below) The subsystems which will go into the ballistic capsule give a good idea of the difficulties facing the planners, designers—and astronauts.

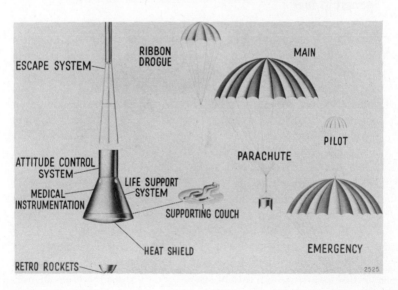

ESCAPE SYSTEM

RIBBON DROGUE

MAIN

PILOT

ATTITUDE CONTROL SYSTEM

LIFE SUPPORT SYSTEM

PARACHUTE

MEDICAL INSTRUMENTATION

SUPPORTING COUCH

HEAT SHIELD

EMERGENCY

RETRO ROCKETS

2525

141

IONIC BEAM RESEARCH:
Some day ionic beams may be used to propel spaceships. The ionic beam in the glowing tube has an effective gas temperature of millions of degrees. This is part of a research study of the effect of high-temperature gases on metals—a problem of the utmost importance in the operation of jet aircraft and rocket ships.

spaceship rotate; the centrifugal force resulting from the motion of flinging away from the axis of rotation would give the passengers a feeling of "gravity" or "weight."

Spaceship fuel

The primary consideration for judging a spaceship fuel is its "specific thrust"—how many pounds of thrust are obtained for every pound of fuel burned in a second? Since the storage problem is acute, the first requirement is for a fuel with a high specific thrust. But each type of fuel has some drawback.

For example, a mixture of liquid hydrogen and fluorine is superior to gasoline in yielding greater speed and carrying a greater payload. But the mixture, which has a specific thrust of almost 400 pounds, is costly and very difficult to handle.

An atomic reactor could supply fuel with a specific thrust of 500 pounds, but it is heavy, bulky and requires shielding from radiation. The chances are that when nuclear fusion (page 176) becomes practicable, it will provide a very superior fuel. It will have a specific thrust of about 1,000 pounds, operating with hydrogen or other light elements, and will present no radiation problems. The difficulty involved in this method is that the atomic particles are expelled at such a high rate of speed that a serious recoil problem is created. Consequently, the question of designing a spaceship to use this fuel is extremely complicated.

Ion propulsion, which makes use of electrified particles, is another method which has some enthusiastic partisans. To build the large spaceships of the future, with payloads of anywhere up to 300,000 pounds, it will probably be necessary to use "clusters" of engines, employing different ones for different purposes.

Solar power is still another suggestion. It is highly efficient, lasting and reliable, and may therefore prove ideal for interplanetary travel. Briefly, the method used would be to mount concave mirrors that focus the sun's rays on boilers which produce steam to run a turbine; the turbine in turn produces electricity. The power thus obtained would ionize (electrify) cesium atoms, and as the positive ions are expelled, the spaceship is driven forward. If the spaceship had large enough surfaces for focusing a substantial amount of sunlight, it might be possible to obtain solar energy directly for propelling it, instead of having to convert the energy.

What would happen if the spaceship left the solar system? Presumably it could get energy from a nearby star or from another solar system.

By-products of space research

The specifications for materials and methods used in space research are so rigorous that scientists are making many valuable discoveries that will benefit everyday life on the earth.

For example, the attempts to reduce the weight and bulk of rockets have resulted in important discoveries of lightweight materials—plastics as well as metal alloys. Similarly, the quest for materials that can withstand unusual heat and shock will lead to useful by-products. Computers are taking over ever more refined functions because the problems posed by space research call for constant improvement in these electronic giants.

Miniaturization of parts often leads to incongruous applications, such as the microscopically sized bearings which can be used in the new dental drills. The research on satellite electronic devices will result in high-fidelity equipment far superior to what is currently available.

The search for superior metals will be reflected in the improvement of surgical instruments and tools. Medical laboratories will benefit by adopting some of the discoveries that are incidental to space research.

The rigorous physical examinations of the successful astronaut candidates have resulted in new techniques and sharper insights into physical health. Doctors are learning more about the human body's ability to resist stress and other unfavorable conditions of the environment. Such problems as the connection between emotional states and proper nutrition are yielding to the intensified research that simulates conditions that will apply to space travel.

Research on these problems is turning into a new science—"bioengineering." This will make it possible to design furniture, automobiles and factory installations for maximum comfort and minimum fatigue. The instruments used to check blood pressure, temperature, metabolism and other physical states of animals in spaceships are much smaller and more accurate than the conventional equipment and are therefore likely to come into regular use.

ANOTHER TRIUMPH OF MINIATURIZATION: Mark Siera holds in one hand his lightweight airborne tape recorder, designed to withstand the extreme accelerations, vibrations and temperatures of space flight. The recorder has an "endless-loop" feature that makes automatic rewinding possible.

Space medical research will undoubtedly stimulate the use of computers in medical work, increase our knowledge of the effect of radiation on living tissue, and result in many other advances.

Navigation is another field which is due to benefit enormously from space research. The United States Navy is spending millions of dollars for work on its Transit navigation satellites. These satellites, spiral-striped balls that will weigh about 50 pounds each, will remain in orbit 400 miles over the earth for five years. When perfected, they will provide man with the most accurate navigation device ever known, and will make sextants and radio beam finders obsolete.

By establishing contact with a Transit satellite, ship and plane navigators will receive information for their computers, almost instantaneously obtaining their position correct to half a mile. The computer used for this purpose will be of quite simple design and will take up very little space.

In the field of photography, too, space research will introduce some remarkable developments. At the Wright Air Development Center, for example, research scientists working for the United States Air Force have made considerable progress toward perfecting an amazing camera that will be attached to a satellite orbiting 300 miles above the earth.

This camera will be so sensitive that it will be able to spot objects as small as 7 feet. It will develop its pictures, put them on electronic tape and then transmit them to a monitoring station on earth. The chief value of this satellite, known as "Samos," will be military, as it will be able to provide otherwise unobtainable information about the activities of an enemy.

But the satellite will also have valuable peacetime uses. Probably the most important will be the opportunity to photograph the sun, planets and stars with a clarity that has never been attained by any of our earthbound equipment. It will also be possible to make detailed observations of the oceans to follow the movement of icebergs, check the location of ships in distress, and carry out scientific surveys.

Life on other planets?

As the likelihood of being able to travel to other planets comes nearer to fulfillment, astronomers are speculating more and more keenly about the chances of finding life on these planets. Formerly relegated to the science-fiction field, this problem is absorbing the attention of some of the world's leading scientists.

For example, Otto Struve, who heads the astronomy department at the University of California, inclines to the view that the Milky Way contains millions of planets on which intelligent life exists. Dr. Struve estimates that there are about 50 billion planets in the Milky Way and that possibly one in 50 has conditions favorable to life. He believes some of them may have beings just as intelligent as man, although he admits there is no direct evidence, and the instruments for observing such planets may never become available.

Most amazing of all, Dr. Struve has suggested that the mighty explosions of stars which take place once in several hundred years may have been the result of nuclear explosions. "It is perfectly conceivable," he has pointed out, "that some intelligent race has meddled once too often with nuclear laws and blown themselves to bits."

Another eminent authority, Dr. Harlow Shapley, former head of the Harvard Observatory, has come to somewhat similar conclusions. He believes that life may exist on certain stars. "Such bodies—I call them Lilliputian stars," Dr. Shapley has said, "might be 100 times as big as Jupiter or 100 times smaller than our sun.

"The heat to support life would come from their interiors and they would not be dependent on a sun, as we are. In such bodies radioactive thorium or potassium might provide a source of energy. I believe some of the energy coming from outer space may originate in this way."

Dr. Shapley puts the minimum number of such bodies in space at 100,000. He conjectures that the beings that may exist on them are quite different from earthlings, as the only light they would have would be faint starlight, and they would be subjected to gravitation and atmospheric pressure vastly more powerful than those prevailing on earth. Fanciful as Dr. Shapley's hypothesis may seem, he has buttressed it with an impressive array of evidence drawn from astronomy, physics, chemistry, mathematics, biology, biochemistry and geology.

Dr. Melvin Calvin of the University of California, probably the world's leading authority on photosynthesis, also believes that life

MERCURY CAPSULE IN ORBIT: An artist's conception of the Mercury capsule in orbit 120 miles over Florida. Project Mercury (pages 140-141) is the pioneer program for putting a manned space vehicle into orbit with subsequent safe recovery.

exists on other planets—possibly on as many as 100 million of them. Dr. Calvin thinks that the conditions on earth which accounted for the origin of life have been present on many other planets. Since man's existence on earth has taken in only a million years of the billions given as the time span of the universe, it seems likely to Dr. Calvin that the life process has had time to develop elsewhere as well.

"Life," he says, "is not a rather special and unique event on one of the minor planets around an ordinary sun at the edge of one of the minor galaxies in the universe"; on the contrary, it may be "a state of matter widely distributed throughout the universe."

To Dr. Calvin the prospect of space travel has far-reaching implications. "There is no reason to suppose that life, and man as its representative, will not transform any planet on which he lands, in the same way, or even in a more profound way than he has transformed the surface of the earth. It might suit him to change the orbit of the moon, and it seems within the realm of possibility that he should be able to do so. When we realize that other organisms may be doing similar things at some millions of regions in the universe,

147

we see that life itself and man, as one representative of that state of organization of matter, becomes a cosmic influence himself."

Late in 1959 Dr. Calvin announced that analysis of meteorites revealed the presence of the structural units of nucleic acid—the substance of which the heredity-transmitting genes are composed. Geneticists incline to the theory that life originated on earth through the effect of cosmic rays, ultraviolet light and electrical storms on fairly simple chemicals. Over many ages the nucleic acids and the process of transmitting hereditary traits were evolved.

If the pre-biological units which later evolved into the nucleic acids are present in meteorites, it seems reasonable to conclude that they are being formed in some non-biological way outside the earth, under the same conditions which led to the origin of life on our own planet.

Life on Mars?

For years scientists have been preoccupied with the problem of whether life exists on Mars. According to Professor Gerard de Vaucouleurs of the Harvard Observatory, evidence obtained from observations on Mars in 1958 "comes very close to being final proof of the existence of some form of plant life on Mars." Observations taken with the 200-inch reflector at the Lowell Observatory in Flagstaff, Arizona, brought out an interesting point: some of the absorption lines in the solar spectrum from the dark areas of the planet indicated the presence of carbon and hydrogen compounds which are found in living matter.

Dr. William Sinton, who carried out the work, was unable to find these three absorption lines in the spectroscopic analysis of any inorganic substance. He did, however, find them characteristic of algae and of filter paper (which contains organic matter in the form of wood pulp or animal fiber).

More recently Professor Ingeborg Schmidt of the University of Indiana has cast serious doubts on the validity of these findings. At the 1959 International Astronautical Congress Professor Schmidt demonstrated that a slide with gray circles on an orange background appeared green. Putting the slide slightly out of focus intensified the greenish effect.

How does this apply to Mars? The previous observers had seen what they took to be green areas characteristic of vegetation. However, Professor Schmidt pointed out that since most of the landscape of Mars has an orange tint, dark areas would look greenish (as demonstrated by the slide). Following up this analogy, she reasoned that blurring caused by the earth's atmosphere would heighten the deceptive effect. Consequently, while she did not deny the possibility of vegetation existing on Mars, she felt that the previous observations were not conclusive.

The mystery cf Venus

Next to the sun and the moon, Venus is the brightest object in the sky. It comes closer to the earth—26 million miles—than any other planet. Its size, mass and orbit are similar to those of the earth. Yet this planet has always remained a mystery because it is completely obscured by clouds.

Up to very recently, the only substance known to be present in the atmosphere of Venus was carbon dioxide, which led astronomers to believe that this planet was very hot (see page 138). If water vapor is present in the atmosphere of Venus, then it is possible that some form of life exists on the planet. Attempts at spectroscopic analysis of the atmosphere of Venus have previously proved futile because observation was distorted by the earth's atmosphere.

Late in 1959, therefore, the National Science Foundation, the Office of Naval Research and Johns Hopkins University sponsored a balloon expedition to penetrate beyond 98 per cent of the earth's atmosphere to a height of 81,000 feet. The telescopic observations made by the expedition seemed to demonstrate clearly that water vapor is present in the atmosphere of Venus, indicating that life may exist on the planet.

A short time later, however, the possibility of liquid water on Venus was flatly denied by Dr. Frank Drake of the National Radio Astronomy Observatory at Green Bank, West Virginia. Dr. Drake's view was based on a three-year study of the planet's radio emissions. Radio waves given off by a heated body are one of the indications of its temperature. In the case of Venus, analysis of its radio emissions indicated a surface temperature of around 585 degrees Fahrenheit. Consequently, Dr. Drake concluded, if there are any seas or lakes on the surface of Venus, they must be of molten metal.

Atomics

Since the late Enrico Fermi put the first rudimentary experimental nuclear reactor in operation on December 2, 1942, atomic research has made giant strides.

Scientists are constantly devising new kinds of specialized reactors to serve specific purposes. They are making notable progress in designing atom-powered vessels, but they are encountering great difficulty in adapting the same principle to plane flight. Radio-isotopes are daily acquiring new and valuable uses. Atom medicine is steadily gaining ground. The idea of converting atomic energy directly into electricity has suggested some remarkable advances which may yet revolutionize power production. And in the field of basic research, scientists are constructing bigger, better and more expensive machines. Most amazing of all, the H-bomb, a dreaded instrument of unparalleled destructiveness, is being gradually tamed for constructive peacetime uses.

NUCLEAR REACTORS

Improved "breeder" reactors

As time goes on, nuclear reactors are becoming more and more specialized. The type that is attracting the most study is the "breeder" reactor, which produces its own atomic fuel at a rate faster than it consumes the atomic "fuel" originally provided for it.

The "fast breeder" which is being built and operated near Detroit by Atomic Power Development Associates will use enriched uranium. The fuel will be made up of one part uranium 235, which fissions, to three parts uranium 238, which does not fission.

The essentials of the breeding process are as follows: the chain reaction releases neutrons which split nuclei of uranium 235 atoms. Every time the nucleus of a uranium 235 atom fissions, 2.5 new neutrons are released. One of these neutrons splits another uranium 235 nucleus, keeping up the chain reaction.

REFUELING A NUCLEAR REACTOR: A technician uses an extended grapple bar to refuel the General Electric Test Reactor (GETR) at the Vallecitos Atomic Laboratory in California. The reactor was the first to be granted a license by the Atomic Energy Commission for private test nuclear reactors. The GETR was built to irradiate test fuel elements and other components of nuclear reactors. Its maximum power capacity is 30,000 kilowatts.

As for the remaining 1.5 neutrons not expended in this way, approximately 1.2 enter the nuclei of the non-fissionable uranium 238 atoms and transmute them into nuclei of plutonium atoms. Plutonium is highly fissionable. Consequently, as this "breeding" process goes on at a compound-interest rate, more fuel is available than was present at the start.

The designers of this reactor estimate that it will use up 87.2 kilograms (about 180 pounds) of uranium 235 in a single year. (To produce the same amount of heat would require 113,750 pounds of coal.) But since each kilogram of uranium 235, as it is consumed, will breed about 1.2 kilograms of plutonium, by the time the 87.5 kilograms of uranium 235 are used up, they will have been replaced by 106 kilograms of plutonium.

The effect is the same as we would get from burning up 113,750 tons of coal and finding that we then have 137,800 tons still available. The efficiency and economy of the breeding process are obvious.

"Thermal breeder" reactors

"Thermal" reactors use a moderator that slows down the speed of neutrons from the rate of 10,000 miles per second to one mile per second. At the latter rate of speed, the reactor becomes much more manageable. This principle of ease of control can be combined with the breeder principle in a "thermal breeder" reactor—with the drawback, however, that uranium is not a suitable fuel in that case. On the other hand, thorium is the ideal fuel for this purpose. Here is how it works:

The thorium fuel in the reactor is transmuted into uranium 233, a fissionable material that does not exist in the natural state. As each atom of uranium 233 fissions, it releases neutrons. Some of these neutrons split more uranium 233 nuclei, keeping up the chain reaction; other neutrons enter the thorium nuclei and continue transmuting them into uranium 233. As this compound-interest process goes on, more fuel (in the form of uranium 233) is left than was originally present (in the form of thorium).

Thorium is three times more abundant in nature than uranium. Using thorium in the thermal breeding reactor would enormously increase the available amount of nuclear fuel. However, thorium is more difficult to extract for commercial use. This is due to the fact

RADIOACTIVE WASTES DISPOSAL: Health physicists from Brookhaven National Laboratory supervise the loading of radioactive wastes on a Navy LST for disposal at sea. No wholly satisfactory disposal method has yet been found.

that thorium is found in low concentrations. The United States has some thorium deposits, but the chief sources are India, Brazil and South Africa.

Plutonium for reactors

The difficulty inherent in using uranium as a nuclear reactor fuel is that uranium 235, which is fissionable, is only 1/140th as plentiful as uranium 238, which is not fissionable. However, as we have seen (page 150), in a breeder reactor the uranium 238 is transmuted into highly fissionable plutonium. It follows, then, that although plutonium does not exist in nature, it is much more plentiful than uranium 235.

Nuclear scientists have therefore devoted intensive study to the processing of plutonium for use as a reactor fuel. The problem is strewn with irksome difficulties, as plutonium is extremely "temperamental." Between room temperature and its melting point, plutonium takes six or more crystal forms and five different solid-state transformations. Each time this happens, its volume and physical properties change.

Nor is this all. Plutonium is an exceedingly dangerous material to handle. In many of its forms it can burst into flame spontaneously, giving off a radioactive smoke that is deadly.

The Argonne National Laboratory has set up a miniature rolling mill to process plutonium and to develop safe handling methods. This plant, which works with plutonium ingots about the size of a bar of soap, is encased in glass and operates in an atmosphere of helium, an inert gas (chemically inactive). Plutonium is continually filtered out, and most of the operations are handled automatically or by remote control.

The men in charge of the Fuel Technology Center feel that these intensive studies and elaborate precautions are worth while, for if plutonium can be made safe, it will vastly increase the available amount of nuclear fuel. An additional advantage will be that reactors using plutonium will be lighter and more compact than present reactors, bringing down the cost of operation.

Portable reactors

The Distant Early Warning (DEW) line, a string of radar stations along the 3,000-mile Arctic frontier, was designed to warn Canada and the United States of surprise air attack. Supplying diesel oil to these remote outposts involves some complicated problems.

To provide a convenient source of light and heat in such bleak situations, the Argonne National Laboratory has perfected the Argonne Low Power Reactor. This "packaged" reactor supplies enough energy to light 300 average homes or heat 30 average homes. It is a highly specialized reactor—a "natural-circulation boiling-water reactor." Instead of producing heat that goes to a heat exchanger and is then passed on to a turbogenerator, the greatly simplified reactor produces steam in its own core.

The reactor fuel is enriched uranium with one supply lasting for three years. It will provide electricity for the radar equipment, as well as light and heat for storehouses, offices and barracks.

The Argonne reactor was designed to be eminently portable because it is intended for use in underdeveloped countries and at remote military posts. Its components can easily be taken apart and reassembled. None of them is larger than 20 feet by 9 feet by 7 feet or weighs more than 10 tons. Consequently it will be a simple matter to fly the reactor parts to any desired location and then assemble them where the reactor is to be used.

DETECTING NUCLEAR EXPLOSIONS

William John Thaler, a young physicist at the Office of Naval Research, has devised a simple radio-monitoring system to detect nuclear explosions and missile launchings anywhere in the world.

The new system is based on the fact that both the ionosphere and the surface of the earth deflect radio signals. (Radar is limited in this respect, as its line-of-sight waves travel in straight lines and therefore cannot be deflected below the horizon.) If a radio transmitter directs its beam upward, the waves will circle the earth, alternately bouncing against the ground and the sky.

As the radio waves go around the earth they are bound to bounce off ionized gases created by a nuclear explosion or missile launching, if either of these has taken place. Sensitive monitoring oscilloscopes would detect such contacts, which could be identified by their own characteristic echo. Experience in operating such a detection system soon makes it possible to distinguish between the differing sounds caused, for example, by lightning, missiles, the aurora borealis, etc.

The system (called Project Tepee after the initials of "Thaler's Project") still requires further development, but it is considered highly promising and worthy of the most careful investigation.

NUCLEAR VESSELS AND PLANES

The first atomic merchant ship

The N.S. (Nuclear Ship) "Savannah," the first nuclear merchant ship, slid down the ways in July 1959. This atom-powered vessel will be capable of cruising 350,000 miles in three and a half years on its original supply of uranium—690 pounds—without refueling.

"SEA LEGS": (Above) This is the name given to the experimental hydrofoil craft being tested by the U.S. Navy's Bureau of Ships. Using two foils, the vessel is capable of speeds of over 25 miles per hour. The intricate control system includes a height-sensing device, gyroscopes, accelerometers, servomechanisms and other electronic equipment. An "autopilot" controls the position of the boat and foils.

HYDROFOIL PRINCIPLE: (Below) The diagram shows why the hydrofoil vessel rises as it moves through the water.

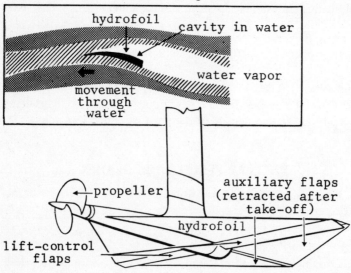

The "Savannah" is not expected to operate at a profit. It will carry 60 passengers and 10,000 tons of cargo, but its main purpose is to demonstrate the safety and practicability of a nuclear-powered ship. The designers have surrounded the nuclear reactor with elaborate safeguards—a ring of water 33 inches thick, a steel cylinder, shielding weighing 2,000 tons, and at the outer rim a collision mat of redwood and steel, two feet thick.

The ship is also equipped with 12 monitors to measure the amount of radiation, which is expected to be no more than normal. As a final precaution, the "Savannah" has been outfitted with a small diesel engine in the unlikely case that the reactor fails.

The first nuclear-powered surface ship

In 1959 the Russians conducted satisfactory dock tests of the first atomic surface ship, the icebreaker "Lenin." The vessel has a displacement of 16,000 tons and can make 19 knots under the most favorable conditions. It is capable of penetrating through six feet of ice. The "Lenin's" three nuclear reactors which power its steam turbines enable it to remain several months at sea without refueling.

The Russians are planning to add three more atomic icebreakers. The fourth and most massive of these would be 525 feet long, with a displacement of 25,000 tons and a cruising speed of 25 knots.

An atomic aircraft carrier

The United States Navy is building the world's first atomic aircraft carrier, the U.S.S. "Enterprise," at Newport News, Virginia, at an estimated cost of $321,000,000. The giant vessel, 1,100 feet long and with a displacement of 85,000 tons, will have eight nuclear reactors to power its four propellers.

Vessels on stilts

Back in 1919 venerable Alexander Graham Bell, the inventor of the telephone, tested a strange-looking vessel which he called the "Hydrodrome Number 4." What made Bell's craft look weird was that it was mounted on hydrofoils, which resembled giant water skis. The test was eminently successful, as the "Hydrodrome" reached the fantastic speed of 71 miles per hour.

After Bell's death in 1922, hydrofoil research practically reached the vanishing point. In recent years, however, the idea of using hydrofoils in combination with nuclear power has been gaining ground.

Charles L. Denison, research coordinator for the Marine Administration, thinks that by 1965 the United States will have a 1,000-ton nuclear hydrofoil liner carrying over 300 passengers at speeds up to 100 miles an hour. Such a vessel would have three 55-foot-long retractable legs or stilts fastened to its hull. Attached to the bottom of these legs would be 31-foot wings that would skim over the water. To economize on shielding, the nuclear engine would ride underwater, making use of the water as a radiation barrier.

While entering or leaving port, such a vessel would maneuver slowly under auxiliary power. Once on the open seas, the stilts would be lowered and the ship would proceed under its nuclear power. The Grumman Aircraft Company is to build a scaled-down non-atomic model in order to provide engineers and designers with more reliable information about hydrofoil ships.

In January 1960 the United States Government ordered an ocean-going hydrofoil ship capable of transporting 100 passengers twice as fast as the speediest ocean liners.

Fleet Ballistic Missiles

The United States Navy is building six atomic submarines in the Fleet Ballistic Missile class. The first of these is the "George Washington." Each submarine will carry 16 Polaris missiles, which have an atomic warhead and a range of 1,200-1,500 miles.

In order to be able to navigate accurately while below the surface, these submarines rely on SINS (Ship Inertial Navigational System). Made up of gyroscopes and accelerometers, this system records every ship motion and transmits to an electronic computer which establishes the submarine's exact position at any given time.

This information in turn goes to the missile control center and a formidable array of 16 electronic brains (the Geo-Ballistic Computer). The function of each computer is to arrange the received information about position and relate it to coded punch cards which contain all essential information about a previously determined target. The combination of these calculations automatically guides the missile to its target.

The equipment of these submarines is so complex and the work so demanding that each of them will have two complete crews. This will make it possible to operate the submarines continuously without wearying either crew to the breaking point.

Submarine tanker

At the Saunders-Roe Company's plant on the Isle of Wight, England, scientists are experimenting with hull designs for an underwater nuclear-powered oil tanker. Such a submarine would not be subject to surface drag or wave resistance; it should therefore make the remarkable speed of 60 knots.

The tanker, with its planned 1,200-foot length (four times that of the "Nautilus," the first nuclear submarine), will have a huge cargo space. The nuclear plant required will be expensive, but the cost will be neutralized by the increase in cargo space through the elimination of coal and oil bunkers.

The high speeds of which the tanker will be capable will make more round trips possible, thus reducing costs. Two clever design features are the utilization of oil cargo or water ballast for partial shielding, and the use of underwater atomic jets which are expected to be more efficient than conventional propellers.

The baffling problems of the atomic plane

The problems of designing and constructing a nuclear-powered plane are so baffling that Dr. Herbert York, research chief of the United States Defense Department, puts the price of success (if it ever comes) at 10 billion dollars—"or some multiple thereof," Dr. York grimly adds. (And yet, since December 1958, after American experts had been working on such a plane for over 12 years, there have been unconfirmed reports that the Russians had a nuclear plane in operation.)

The advantages of such a plane are theoretically attractive. The power value of one pound of uranium 235 is fantastically greater than a corresponding amount of any conventional fuel. There is no doubt that a nuclear-powered bomber would be capable of making a round trip to and from any spot in the world without having to land or refuel. There are other military advantages: the plane could function as a supersonic bomber, as a patrol unit, and as a platform for launching missiles.

Against these advantages, there are several disadvantages that have continued to frustrate some of the finest scientific minds. The chief problem is the shielding required to protect the crew from radiation emitted by the nuclear reactor. The kind of materials needed for shielding—lead, steel, concrete—would weigh about 50,000 pounds (This is on the assumption that the shielding is distributed in the most efficient manner.)

The gross weight of the largest B-52 bomber is over 400,000 pounds. Partly because of the shielding, the nuclear plane would have to be larger and heavier, say 500,000 pounds. This in turn would require special runways, since none now in existence would be suitable for the giant plane.

A nightmare possibility to be considered is that of a crash, on taking off or landing, for example, or in a mid-air collision. Because a reactor constantly produces highly radioactive fission materials, such a crash would contaminate a large area for a long time.

There are still other obstacles to be considered. Engineers have yet to find materials that can withstand the heat generated by a nuclear reactor. Again, the problems of servicing a "hot" nuclear plane after landing seem insurmountable. There is still another unpleasant possibility: how safe would a nuclear plane be against heat-sensitive infrared defensive missiles which could be expected to make their way into the plane's exhaust stacks and explode there? In any event, this "dinosaur" plane may turn out to be obsolete in an era of unmanned missiles.

USES OF ATOMIC ENERGY

Distilling sea water

As population increases, the problem of adequate water supply becomes more critical every year. Experts in this field believe that the best way to provide for expanded water needs is to construct plants that will use atomic energy to distill fresh water from the ocean. The United States Department of the Interior has proposed one such installation in California as a pilot plant. Department officials believe that eventually it will be cheaper to convert sea water than to tap fresh-water reserves.

Processing radioisotopes

The Budd Company, which concentrates mainly on the manufacture of automobile body components and stainless-steel railway cars, has been licensed by the Atomic Energy Commission to run the first commercial facility for fabricating high-strength radioisotopes. These substances release radiation which is being used for a growing variety of purposes.

The radioisotopes are prepared in "pellets" and "wafers" and encapsulated in small metal containers. Mechanical hands then insert these containers into machines which operate like X-ray machines to detect and measure defects in materials.

In order to render efficient service, the plant maintains a bulk inventory of the isotopes in current use. More than 1,500 firms are using these isotopes, and the number of users grows daily. It has been calculated that the increasing use of these radioactive materials saves industrial firms more than a billion dollars a year.

Some radioisotope applications

Radioisotopes have thousands of uses, and there seems to be no limit to the new applications constantly being discovered. One of the most popular uses of radioisotopes is in checking products that must be of rigorously specified dimensions.

A radioisotope emits gamma rays of known strength. These are directed through the material being tested. Whenever the strength of the radiation coming through the material varies, it is clear that the specimen being examined does not come up to specifications.

Flaws are also discovered by making a film of the radiation. When the film is viewed, any flaws will at once become obvious.

Large savings are being realized in bridge construction through the use of radioisotopes to check the strength of welding work. Radioisotopes are important in the periodic examination of aircraft parts to conform with government safety laws. Door frames, landing gear, stabilizers, propellers and wing spars are among the equipment checked in this manner.

In building the huge and costly aircraft carrier U.S.S. "Enterprise," radioisotope checking was employed countless times to rule out flaws that would have caused short circuits. Radioisotope examination is also important in making the heavy castings that are used in nuclear reactors.

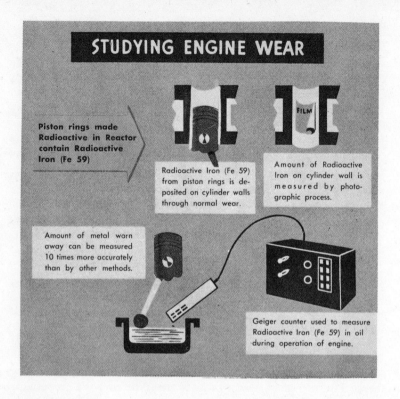

STUDYING ENGINE WEAR

Piston rings made Radioactive in Reactor contain Radioactive Iron (Fe 59)

Radioactive Iron (Fe 59) from piston rings is deposited on cylinder walls through normal wear.

Amount of Radioactive Iron on cylinder wall is measured by photographic process.

Amount of metal worn away can be measured 10 times more accurately than by other methods.

Geiger counter used to measure Radioactive Iron (Fe 59) in oil during operation of engine.

Several American railroad systems are now using atomic warning-lamps. The lamp contains a radioactive gas, krypton 85, which is sealed in. The inner part of the lens is coated with phosphor crystals that cause luminescence in the radioactive gas so that the lamp acts as an automatic warning signal. The installation of these lamps has resulted in considerable operating savings, and new uses are being found for them. The lamps operate for ten years without replacement.

Medical uses of radioisotopes are discussed on pages 165-168.

Radiation for "dirty" diamonds

The diamond trade has little use for yellow or brown diamonds, which are considered undesirable. Having little market value as jewelry, they were destined for industrial use. But with the coming of the nuclear age the appearance of the diamonds can be changed by radiation from a nuclear reactor.

The research reactor at Brookhaven National Laboratory emits neutrons which give discolored diamonds a greenish tint. A cyclotron which produces beta rays colors the diamonds blue. In either case, the color change results from the impact of the atomic particles on the gem's crystal structure. The diamonds exposed in this way do not become radioactive and remain perfectly safe to use.

Irradiating deserts and polar regions

Scientists have worked intensively on the idea of using radiation to create plants hardy enough to grow in the desert and arctic regions. If successful, this method would enormously increase the world's food supply.

Professor Ake Gustavsson, a Swedish geneticist, has pointed out that "barley is very much what it was 500,000 years ago. Now by radiation we can remake its chromosomes and modernize it. We can get quite new chromosomes. We can change the parent plants and produce progeny which will go on breeding with qualities quite different from the original type."

To bring about the desired changes, the scientists would make use of cosmic rays and man-made atomic rays. The latter would include (a) atomic particles from accelerators; (b) gamma rays from the radioisotope cobalt 60; (c) neutrons from nuclear reactors.

The same methods are being applied to make plants more resistant to disease. In the United States alone, the annual toll from plant disease comes to over 3 billion dollars.

Sterilizing the soil

Sterilizing an acre of soil by chemical means prior to planting costs anywhere from $300 to $500. A portable nuclear reactor can do the same job more effectively for about $70 an acre. According to Drs. Samuel G. Wildman and Amos Norman of the University of California, the neutrons and gamma rays from the reactor kill such crop-destroying parasites as nematodes, fungi and insects; the rays prevent reproduction of the parasites and also prevent weed seeds from germinating.

As the reactor can operate by remote control, the shielding problem would be comparatively simple. The radioactivity caused by the reactor would not last long enough to affect the soil or the crops eventually grown in it.

A radiation machine

Radiation can also be used to improve the quality of many kinds of products. A machine that works as an electron accelerator for this purpose sells for about $60,000. It is expected to make possible many new products and processes. Its uses include sterilizing drugs and cosmetics, and preserving and processing food. It is also expected to be useful in vulcanizing rubber and in chemical and plastic research.

Atomic timekeeping

The accuracy of scientific observations and calculations is at the mercy of the scientists' timekeeping methods. That is why they are always interested in new devices that give promise of more precise timekeeping. So far they have succeeded in developing clocks with a margin of error of one second in 300 years. But their goal is a clock that is much more accurate than that.

In their search for precision, the scientists have turned to atomic clocks. One such clock, devised by Professor Jerrold R. Zacharias of Massachusetts Institute of Technology, is so accurate that according to various estimates it will lose no more than a second in 3,000 years.

This 500-pound clock, which will probably sell eventually for about $10,000, will be of great importance in such fields as astronomical observation, long-range navigation, radio and other types of communication, surveying and military map making.

The heart of this "Atomichron" is the cesium atom, which, when heated to the temperature of boiling water, vibrates 9,200,000,000 times a second. The count is computed electronically to keep time.

Dr. Harold Lyons of the Hughes Aircraft Company has also designed an atomic clock. When the clock has been completed and has satisfactorily passed tests, it will be placed in an orbiting satellite moving at a speed of 18,000 miles an hour. The timepiece, which operates with the ammonia molecule, is a maser clock. ("Maser" stands for Microwave Amplification by Stimulated Emission of Radiation.)

The reason for orbiting this atomic clock is to broadcast its time readings to a ground station. There the readings will be compared with the time on a similar model on the ground. Whatever differences may develop in the readings will be checked against the differences predicted by the special and general theories of relativity. (According to these theories, a clock in motion and a clock at rest should keep time differently.) In this way scientists will be able to check the accuracy of predictions based on Einstein's relativity theories.

All atomic clocks depend on a vibrating atom or molecule to supply the "ticking." This is made possible by the fact that each kind of atom or molecule has its own characteristic rate of vibration. The nitrogen atom in ammonia, for example, vibrates or "ticks" 24 billion times a second. An electronic current synchronizes these vibrations with the much slower vibrations of a low-frequency clock employing a quartz crystal. The synchronization of the minute hand and the second hand on a conventional clock illustrates the principle involved.

THE GROWTH OF ATOM MEDICINE

In the last ten years the use of atom medicine has become so widespread that every major American medical center uses some form of it in diagnosis and treatment. This includes a thousand hospitals that have had highly successful results with radioactive iodine for thyroid cases. The over-all use of atom medicine is becoming so important that by 1980 one out of every three patients will be receiving atomic diagnosis or treatment.

The chief medical use of radioisotopes is against cancer, with cobalt 60 as the favored form of treatment. At least 200,000 cancer victims are being treated every year with radiocobalt, which in many ways is superior to X-ray treatment. The radioisotope entails smaller doses, and can be concentrated more accurately on the cancerous cells. In addition, it is far less likely to cause burns or harmful radiation effects. Atomic pellets and atomic "thread" are also used to reach organs where it would otherwise be difficult to obtain access to the cancer.

A reactor for medical use

The world's first atomic medical center is in operation at Brookhaven National Laboratory. The purpose of this medical center is to

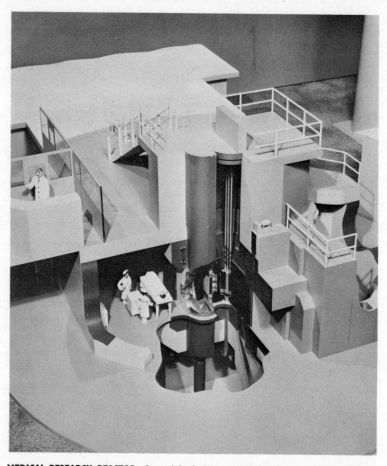

MEDICAL-RESEARCH REACTOR: A model of the medical-research reactor at Brookhaven National Laboratory, the first of its kind. The core of the reactor is highly enriched uranium 235 surrounded by aluminum. The shielding for the reactor is made up of steel, lead and concrete. Shutters can be opened in the shielding to obtain beams of neutrons under carefully controlled conditions. These beams will be used for research in treating human patients under special safeguards, and also for animal research in another part of the building.

apply the most effective radiation techniques to the treatment of disease. To make this possible, Brookhaven uses a nuclear reactor specially designed for medical use and biological research.

The new reactor delivers a neutron beam of 50 times greater intensity than was previously available. This reduces exposure time, enhances the reactor's usefulness and provides flexibility in choosing types of treatment.

While the treatment of tumors is the most urgent purpose for which the reactor is intended, it will also be used for basic research into the effectiveness of radioisotopes in medical diagnosis and treatment.

Next to the reactor core are two irradiated rooms, one for patients and one for experimental animals. These rooms are heavily shielded. In the reactor's shielding there are neutron apertures which are automatically opened and closed by hydraulic shutters.

The study of the effects of radiation on laboratory animals will undoubtedly have important effects in saving human lives. The range of experimental therapy techniques studied includes antibiotics, fresh whole-blood transfusions, careful feeding and expert nursing care.

The medical center assembles its staff from all over the country. When these staff members eventually return to their own communities, hospitals and laboratories they will transmit to others the knowledge and skill they have acquired in the Brookhaven atomic medicine center.

Radioisotopes for diagnosis

In some cases of fractured thigh or dislocated hip bones, it is vital for the surgeon to know whether an injured bone has "died" from loss of blood supply. Hitherto it has been necessary to take several months, perhaps as much as a year, for the accurate diagnosis that makes satisfactory treatment possible.

A research team at the Orthopedic Surgery Department of the University of Pittsburgh has discovered how to obtain the desired information in a few minutes by using a radioisotope—sodium 24. When this "tracer" is pumped into the injured bone, it retains its radioactivity if the bone is "dead."

On the other hand, in still-living bone, the blood dilutes the radioactivity of the tracer within ten minutes. Consequently, measuring the amount of radioactivity left gives the surgeon the information he needs about the condition of the injured bone.

Diagnosing heart ailments

Two Israeli scientists, Dr. Fritz Dreyfuss and Dr. Abraham Hochman, have announced that the onset of coronary thrombosis (blood clotting in the coronary arteries) can be detected and located by the use of radioactive iodine. The technique depends on the fact that this isotope is attracted to inflamed tissues and abscesses.

Electrocardiograms do not always reveal the occurrence of a heart attack. The use of the radioactive iodine is more dependable in this respect; and, because the tracer pinpoints the location of the blood clot, it is helpful in diagnosis and treatment.

Proton beams for brain operations

Some cases of severe pain and depression can be relieved by a brain operation that involves cutting several nerve tracts. In 1958 surgeons performed this operation for the first time with an "atomic knife"—a proton beam that required no incision into the brain.

Whereas the conventional operation requires weeks of preparation and weeks of recovery, the atomic operation took about two hours; as soon as it was over, the patient walked off to a meal. He had experienced no pain and complained only of some weariness at having been strapped in the same position for two hours.

During the operation, which took place in a Stockholm hospital, the patient was rotated from time to time so that the beam from the synchrocyclotron could strike the brain from different angles. The surgeons directed the beam by remote control, giving the patient instructions from time to time by telephone.

The proton beam, shaped by two focusing magnets, two magnetic coils and a rectangular aperture, was 10 millimeters wide and 2 millimeters thick. The destroyed nerve tissues were 3 millimeters thick.

THERMOELECTRICITY

A portable electric generator

The problem of converting heat directly into electricity is one that has long fascinated scientists. The familiar way to produce electricity is by means of generators that are powered by steam turbines, gas engines or water power. Hence the development of the SNAP III generator is of the greatest interest. (The name of the device is derived from "System for Nuclear Auxiliary Power Program of the Aircraft Reactors Group.")

This remarkably efficient device weighs 5 pounds; it has a diameter of $4\frac{3}{4}$ inches and a height of $5\frac{1}{2}$ inches. Its job is to convert radiation from a radioactive material—polonium 210—into 5 watts of electricity. The generator has no moving parts and operates by means of thermocouples.

In its simplest terms, a thermocouple is made up of semi-conductors (two unlike metals that are good conductors of electricity but poor conductors of heat). When heat is applied to the two joined metals and a wire is attached to the two open ends, an electrical current flows between these ends.

The amount of energy emitted by radioactive substances is calculated in terms of half-lives—the amount of time it takes for half the energy to be released. Polonium 210 has a half-life of 140 days. At the end of this period, the reduction of radioactivity reduces the electrical output from 5 watts to 3 watts.

In all, during the first two half-lives of 280 days, the generator produces as much electricity as could be obtained from 1,500 pounds of the best conventional batteries.

Many other radioactive materials can be substituted for polonium. The radioisotopes which have a longer half-life would furnish more electricity for a longer time. The first model of the generator cost about $15,000; the future cost will come down to $200.

As for the polonium, it is valued at $30,000,000 for less than a gram. A similar amount of other suitable radioactive material, however, would cost about $600. The enormous amount of radio-active material from nuclear wastes could very well serve as a source of atomic power for the generator.

Scientists originally developed the device as a light, compact power source for instruments carried in earth satellites. They will probably find many other uses for the generator. At its first public demonstration on President Eisenhower's desk it was used to spin a miniature plane propeller and to power a small radio transmitter and receiver.

Electricity from a nuclear reactor

One of the most ambitious projects of nuclear scientists is to convert the enormous amount of heat energy liberated in a nuclear

MAGNIFICENT RESEARCH TOOL: A section of the great Alternating Gradient Synchrotron being constructed at Brookhaven National Laboratory. Shown here are a few of the 240 powerful magnets that will be needed to keep atomic particles on their course as they circle through a half-mile-long tunnel. In the span of one second the particles will circle the magnet ring over 350,000 times. Each time the particles pass one of 12 radio-frequency amplifiers, they will receive an extra 1000 electron volts of energy. By the time they complete the course they will be travelling faster than 186,000 miles per second.

reactor into electricity at a cost which compares favorably with the cost of conventional methods.

For a long time it seemed that the nuclear reactor was only a highly expensive substitute for a coal-fired furnace. The heat energy released by the reactor was used to make steam in order to create mechanical energy in generators which in turn produced electrical energy. This method is wasteful and costly—hence the search for a method of directly converting heat energy into electrical energy without moving parts.

Experiments at the Los Alamos Scientific Laboratory finally resulted in a successful pioneering attempt to produce electricity directly. As in the case of the SNAP III generator, the thermocouple principle is the secret of the new process. The two metals used are uranium and cesium.

The heat released by the reactor changes the cesium metal into a gas. The gaseous cesium in this state is known as a "plasma." This plasma has about a thousand times the thermal force of any solid metal.

The other metal (uranium) is a little rod less than an inch long and a quarter of an inch in diameter. This is connected to a small metal can which contains the cesium and is enclosed in a cooling system.

When the equipment is lowered into the core of a reactor, neutrons from the reactor bombard the uranium 235, making it fission and give off intense heat which converts the cesium into a gas and strips off its electrons. Establishing contact between the hot junction of the cesium gas and uranium (2,000 degrees Centigrade) and the "cold" junction of the cesium and the coolant (300 degrees Centigrade) produces an electric current.

This thermocouple arrangement produces 40 watts of electricity— enough to power a light bulb. While the process is revolutionary, it is still in a primitive state and capable of considerable improvement and elaboration. Further experiment will undoubtedly result in greater and longer power production and a variety of uses. These possibilities include marine and space flight propulsion.

ATOMIC RESEARCH

A two-mile accelerator

In recent years circular accelerators (cyclotrons) of atomic particles have monopolized attention. But linear (straight-line) accelerators have their advantages too. One of them is that they are more efficient in accelerating electrons than circular machines are. The explanation is that when the electrons travel in a circular path, some of the huge energy used to propel them is radiated away. This is not true of linear accelerators.

This is one of the reasons why the Atomic Energy Commission is planning to build the longest of all linear accelerators at Stanford University. The huge machine, two miles long, will start with energies of between 10 and 15 billion electron volts. Eventually, if current plans materialize, the energy will gradually be raised to 45 bev. (A bev is a unit equal to 10 billion electron volts.) This enormous increase in the force propelling the electrons should naturally yield much more valuable research results.

The force to be applied is so great that the electrons would travel at 99.9999999 per cent of the speed of light (186,000 miles per second). According to Einstein's relativity theories, the weight of the electrons will increase 30,000 times during the trip. Since collision with air molecules would slow up the electrons, the tube will first be pumped free of air. This would result in a remarkably high vacuum —one-trillionth of a normal atmosphere.

The accelerator will be housed in two parallel tunnels 35 feet below ground and separated from each other by several feet of earth. One tunnel will contain the equipment. In the other tunnel will be the empty tube through which the electrons will be propelled by a radio-frequency wave to strike with terrific force at nuclei of target

GIANT BUBBLE CHAMBER: This enables scientists to photograph the trails left by invisible particles of matter.

atoms. The cost of the huge machine is reckoned at $118,000,000; it should be completed no later than 1966.

The two-mile length will make it possible to position a series of 240 klystron electronic tubes to do the accelerating of the electrons, which works in this manner: the first of the series of tubes is positively charged, attracting the negatively charged electrons. But as the electrons pass the klystron tube, its charge is changed to negative, repelling the electrons and forcing them ahead. This switching process is repeated with each klystron tube, forcing the electrons to pick up additional speed each time. The longer they travel, the faster they move—hence the two-mile length.

Burying the tunnel at a depth of 35 feet will prevent escape of dangerous radiation. One of the earliest projects will be measuring the size of the atomic nucleus. This will be a notable achievement in increasing our knowledge of the structure of matter.

Another result of the terrific atomic impacts should be a greatly simplified knowledge of atomic structure—much clearer than the present baffling situation, with 26 different kinds of subatomic particles that scientists are trying to account for.

The biggest bubble chamber

The six-foot bubble chamber used in connection with the 6 billion-volt Bevatron at the University of California is one of the most complicated and most dangerous scientific instruments in the world. Beams of atomic particles forced through an accelerator at speeds approaching the speed of light are whirled into the huge bubble chamber filled with 150 gallons of liquid hydrogen.

As the particles stream through the liquid, they leave faint trails which are photographed to supply scientists with some of nature's best-hidden secrets about the properties of matter.

Liquid hydrogen is very difficult to handle. It is so cold that it boils at −252.7 degrees Centigrade at atmospheric pressure. It vaporizes if not kept refrigerated. The slightest leak will cause an explosion. The quantity of liquid hydrogen kept in the huge bubble chamber has the explosive power of 1,500 pounds of TNT.

When Dr. Luis Alvarez decided to use this dangerous liquid in a bubble chamber, he started cautiously with a chamber of half-inch diameter. Step by step he worked up to a 10-inch chamber, carefully

EXTRAORDINARY COMPLEXITY: These views of the great bubble chamber at the Lawrence Radiation Laboratory of the University of California give an awe-inspiring impression of the planning and designing genius that went into its construction.

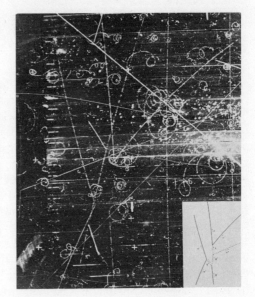

NATURE'S SCRAWLS: A typical photograph from a bubble chamber. To the layman these lines mean nothing; to the trained scientist they are rich in significance. We owe our knowledge of anti-matter, for example, to bubble-chamber photos. Esoteric as such discoveries seem, they will eventually turn out to have practical applications (see page 177).

installing safety devices in the laboratory to guard against accidents. But the results obtained through the use of liquid hydrogen emboldened Dr. Alvarez to take a truly daring step—the construction of a six-foot-long bubble chamber at a cost of $2,000,000.

The project involved incredible difficulties. The electromagnet surrounding the chamber weighs 200 tons. It cannot be maneuvered on wheels, as they are too unstable. Instead, the magnet was outfitted with four huge mechanical feet which give it the uncanny appearance of a mechanical dinosaur. Countless leak detectors had to be installed to warn of escaping hydrogen. Inside the chamber there are 104 alarm circuits to flash lights, honk horns and ring bells at the slightest sign of anything going amiss.

If anything does go seriously wrong, it will be possible to dispose of the whole supply of liquid hydrogen through a pipe that empties into a canyon. The scientists have even provided against an explosion by using a plastic roof that will blow off easily, allowing the blast to force its way up and thus minimize the impact of the explosion. All these difficulties are considered worth putting up with because of the priceless information the scientists hope to obtain about the properties of matter.

CONTROLLED FUSION AND ITS USES
Taming the hydrogen bomb

Atomic *fission* is the *splitting* of *heavy* atoms (uranium) that takes place in the atomic bomb or in a nuclear reactor. In the atomic bomb, fission is used for destructive purposes; in a reactor, fission is controlled in order to achieve some constructive purpose, such as producing power, forming radioisotopes or conducting research.

Atomic *fusion* is the *combining* of *light* atoms (hydrogen) that takes place in the hydrogen or thermonuclear bomb. So far this process has been employed only for destructive purposes. In order to adapt fusion to peacetime purposes, scientists must learn to control the fusion process. They have been hampered by two difficulties.

One difficulty is the temperature required—on the order of several hundred million degrees. The second is that the controlled fusion process forms a gas that must be contained in some manner. To devise a leak-proof container is a baffling problem.

The temperature needed for the fusion processes lasts only a tiny fraction of a millionth of a second. This is long enough for an explosion, but too short for a controlled reaction. But suppose it were feasible to obtain this temperature. Then the problem of fashioning an appropriate container would still remain to be solved; even the most resistant containing material would vaporize at a little over 6,000 degrees Centigrade. Hence no material vessel will do the trick.

Yet the theoretical possibilities of controlling the fusion process are attractive, as all the necessary hydrogen "fuel" can be obtained from deuterium, a heavier form of hydrogen which is easily available from the ocean and which is perfectly suited to the fusion process.

The ideal method of attacking the container problem is to form the container from a magnetic "bottle." The procedure is to electrify the deuterium gas at high temperatures and then, by means of a powerful electrical field, squeeze the electrified gas into a narrow beam.

Scientific laboratories in the United States, England and the Soviet Union have applied themselves to the problem for several years with a number of limited successes. If the reaction proceeds as it should, vast quantities of neutrons are released. A number of experimenters have announced such a result, but in each case there has been a strong possibility that the neutrons were what are termed "false neutrons"—not the real thermonuclear neutrons which would be produced by successful fusion.

The latest of these experiments was announced in August 1959. It took place at the Naval Research Laboratory in Washington, D.C., under the direction of Dr. Alan C. Kolb. The basic item of the complicated equipment is a simple glass tube about one foot long and 1.2 inches in diameter. Around the tube is a magnetic coil which has the job of confining the gas in the tube.

The first step is to pump deuterium gas into the tube. The gas is then electrified, breaking it down into positively and negatively charged particles so that it can be subjected to the magnetic field. Now a huge bank of condensers delivers 30,000,000,000 watts of electricity through the magnetic coil.

This powerful thrust forces the deuterium gas away from the sides of the tube and toward the center and in one-millionth of a second heats it to a temperature of 3,000,000 degrees. These electrical reactions, taking 10-millionths of a second, heat the gas to a temperature of 15,000,000 degrees and release millions of neutrons as the deuterium particles are squeezed together.

Does this mean that successful fusion has taken place? The director of the experiment has cautiously refrained from an outright assertion to that effect. He does believe, however, that the results are interesting and encouraging and very possibly the nearest that man has come to bringing about controlled fusion.

The studies of controlled fusion have led to a new subdivision of physics, called "magnetohydrodynamics" or "hydromagnetics." This deals with the problems of electrically conducting fluids or gases in the presence of electrical fields. While this sounds highly theoretical, it has already acquired a vitally important application in the studies on workable defenses against ballistic missiles.

The problem here is to create magnetic fields to deflect incoming missiles. Dr. Russel M. Kulsrud, a member of the fusion team at Princeton University, believes that if the incoming object is electrically responsive, it can be stopped by the use of a magnetic field. So far, however, these studies are in the theoretical stage.

Some of the uses to which fusion could be put are still in the realm of the fantastic. It might be possible, for example, to apply this process to step up food production enormously by growing algae or by relying on chemical means to build up synthetic foods. Another possible use would be the adoption of new mining methods to delve hundreds of miles into the earth in order to get a much larger supply of the rare metals which are being increasingly used in modern technology.

But other suggestions for using the fusion process are less visionary. In many areas, for example, there are oil deposits in which the oil is too thick to be worked by present conventional methods. An under-surface H-bomb explosion would release the trapped oil, enabling it to flow freely. It is said that in the Athabaska Lake region in northern Canada, there is an area worth $100,000,000 a square mile if the oil it contains can be released.

It is also possible to obtain oil from shale formations. Under present conditions it would be highly unprofitable to mine the shale, heat it to extract the oil and then get rid of the useless rock. On the other hand, an H-bomb explosion under the shale would generate enormous heat, making the oil available for pumping and at the same time bypassing the problem of removing the rock.

There are many arid regions on the globe where water runs off because it cannot penetrate the ground. Here too an under-surface explosion would smash up the underlying rock, making it possible for water to flow into the earth and be stored in huge underground reservoirs. Dr. Harold Brown, an associate director of the Atomic Energy Commission's laboratory at Livermore, California, believes that one H-bomb explosion would make it possible to store 70 billion gallons of water.

Another suggested use for underground H-bomb explosions is the creation of heat reservoirs. In all such cases a prodigious amount of heat would be trapped underground. By bubbling a gas through the rock, or by forcing in water and drawing it off as steam, this heat could be used to produce electricity.

Underground explosions could also produce radioisotopes in much larger quantities than are currently supplied by nuclear reactors. Since the uses for these radioisotopes are increasing all the time, this new source of supply could fill a growing need.

Scientists at the Livermore laboratory believe "it will be entirely possible to carve a 300-foot-deep harbor and entrance channel in ice-locked northern Alaska by means of four carefully spaced H-bomb blasts." Dr. Gerald Johnson, an associate director of the laboratory, has stated that the complete cost "might be about one-tenth the cost of conventional methods." The creation of a harbor in this way would open up the hinterland to settlement and make it possible to exploit the region's rich store of valuable minerals.

The nuclear blasts would have to be preceded by a great deal of study. Rocks differ in their ability to absorb radiation; hence a careful examination of the rock under the coastline is essential. The hardness of the rock is another important factor, for it would help determine the strength of the nuclear blasts required. And, most vital of all, careful calculations would be needed to find out how long it would take before the released radioactivity would be dissipated to tolerable limits.

Using anti-matter

In the fission of heavy elements and the fusion of light elements we release only about 1 per cent of the energy contained in the nuclear mass. Matter as we understand it is made up of a positively charged nucleus around which negatively charged electrons revolve. In 1955 physicists discovered the negatively charged nucleus. Further experiments showed that when negatively charged nuclei ("anti-matter") collide with positively charged nuclei, they completely destroy each other; mass energy is converted into energy of motion. Two-thirds of the energy thus released is converted into heat. Theoretically, at least, this process offers a new source of power.

Eventually scientists may find out how to utilize anti-matter as the most efficient fuel of all, particularly where a lightweight fuel is desired. In this connection we think of space travel, which requires the lightest efficient fuel. Fantastic problems will turn up and give rise to equally fantastic solutions.

For example, if "anti-iron" were used as a fuel, it could be stored by forming a magnet of anti-matter and keeping it suspended in a vacuum by enclosing it in an electromagnetic field. To remove the fuel as needed, a special form of magnetic tongs would have to be devised.

How would scientists produce anti-matter in usable quantities?

Right now it would cost over $1,000,000,000,000 to produce one ounce of anti-matter. Obviously this is a problem that will take years to solve. One scientist has advanced the daring speculation that somewhere in the universe there may exist galaxies composed of anti-matter, which could be obtained by space expeditions and brought back to earth.

Television

Space satellites for long-range communication

Engineers of the Bell Telephone Laboratories have been working for some time on a method of using earth satellites as reflecting mirrors for long-distance telephone and television communication. The plan calls for using balloon satellites to bounce signals from Holmdel, New Jersey to Goldstone, California or the reverse. This method, if successful, would make transoceanic telecasting feasible.

The New Jersey transmitter makes use of a 60-foot "dish" parabolic antenna to aim beams of microwave signals at passing satellites. The signals which bounce off the satellites can be picked up by a powerful directional antenna. In this case the signals will be received by the 85-foot dish antenna at Goldstone, operated by the Jet Propulsion Laboratory of the National Aeronautics and Space Administration.

At Holmdel a large horn-shaped antenna is being built to receive signals from Goldstone. Such an antenna has the same parabolic shape as a dish antenna, but it reflects the signals down into a horn instead of focusing the radio waves on an open-air receiver. The purpose of the horn is to eliminate interference from extraneous radio waves.

A maser system, a device for enormously increasing the sensitivity of receivers, is an important part of the horn antenna. The core of the maser is a ruby crystal bathed in liquid helium at a temperature of 460 degrees below zero Fahrenheit. The installation has a clever device for draining off the helium as it vaporizes and returning it to be used over again.

The engineers expect to put balloons with aluminized surfaces in orbit near the poles at an elevation of about 1,000 miles. The satellites will be equipped to send orbital data which will be fed into electronic computers to control the directional beam of the antennas.

COMMUNICATION VIA MAN-MADE SATELLITES: Artist's conception of the transmission of telephone messages by space satellite, to be tested in Project Echo. The horn antenna designed by Bell Telephone Laboratories is a highly efficient directional receiver. The satellite which will act as a reflector for communications is pictured on page 123.

It will also be possible to track the satellites, either by radar or by equipping the satellites with radio beacons.

Due to the comparative lightness of these satellites, they are expected to be affected by gravity and density variations in space, making them more erratic than earlier, heavier satellites. To guard against this anticipated erratic orbital behavior, it would be necessary to have some 20 satellites in space so that at least one of them would always be accessible to signals.

Russian scientists are also planning to use satellites for telecasting, but their technique is somewhat different. They expect to place a satellite in a "hovering" orbit approximately 22,400 miles from the earth. Placed over the equator, the satellite would take exactly one day to make the circuit of its orbit. As this is the same amount of time the earth takes to rotate on its axis, the satellite would remain over the same region, the scientists having selected Indonesia for this purpose.

The required distance was calculated in the following manner. A satellite placed 300 miles from the earth takes about an hour and a half for a complete circuit. The moon, 240,000 miles away, takes a month. The distance of 22,400 miles is the one at which an orbiting satellite would take a day for its circuit.

In order to keep the electronic equipment of the satellite operating continuously, it would be outfitted with chemical and solar batteries. While the satellite is on the sunny side of the earth, the solar batteries would recharge the chemical batteries.

In time, space may become overloaded with radio signals emanating from outmoded satellites. In that case, the problem of recapturing and dismantling these satellites may become acute.

Telecasting via trans-Atlantic cable

The engineers of the British Broadcasting Corporation have developed a method of transmitting television pictures from Great Britain to the United States via the trans-Atlantic cable used for telephone messages. Transmission time is 100 minutes, far quicker than the facsimile method of relaying still photographs.

This is a remarkable technical achievement, as conventional television signals require a broad channel, whereas telephone signals travel on a narrow channel. American television channels operate on 4,000,000 cycles per second, while in Great Britain a channel of 3,000,000 cycles per second is standard. To make use of the telephone cable it was necessary to compress the electronic signals into a channel of 4,500 cycles per second.

The problem is to compress the amount of electronic information very sharply, yet in such a way that the resulting television picture still retains enough definition to be of practical value. One effect of the narrow channel, for example, is that it cuts down the amount of movement that is permissible on the screen. (Movement that is too rapid or far-ranging will cause blur.) Initially the chief value of the new technique will be in news telecasts, with the strong possibility that viewers in such widely separated cities as Rome and Los Angeles could see the same program on the same day. Unlike other plans for large-scale telecasting that have been broached previously, this one is economically quite practicable.

A new television antenna

For several years scientists of the General Ceramics Corporation have been working on a cheap, compact television antenna that is destined to replace the unsightly conventional antenna. The new type of antenna, which is about the size of a large cigar and has a few coils of wire wound around it, is made up of a ferrite.

Widely used in television transformers, radar equipment, telephone filters and electronic-computer "memories," ferrites are substances that combine iron oxide (rust) with the oxide of one or more other metals. The additional metal, for example, may be cobalt, copper, magnesium, manganese, nickel or zinc. Ferrites have already been used for some time for the antennas of transistorized radios, some television circuits, police radios and airborne communication systems.

"I believe that a ferrite antenna installed inside the receiver cabinet and having the necessary selectivity and sensitivity is just a short way off," said Henry A. Arnhold of the General Ceramics Corporation in May 1959. "This would mean lower costs for the antenna assembly, elimination of installation and maintenance costs and an esthetically more desirable product." The new type of television antenna is expected to come into general use in 1961.

A special television lens

Some kinds of television equipment used for observation of industrial processes have to be able to withstand terrific heat. To meet this need, the General Electric Corporation has developed a television lens that can provide a clear picture of the flames inside a boiler where the temperature goes beyond 2,000 degrees Fahrenheit.

Housed in a 14-inch steel tube and cooled by a steady stream of compressed air, this specialized lens resists melting when used in boilers and other hot areas.

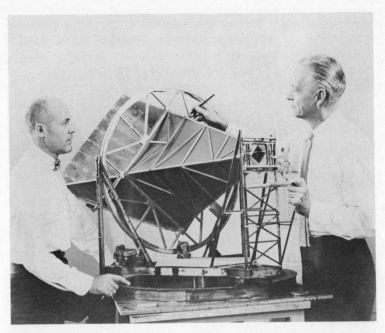

NOVEL ANTENNA: A close-up view of a model of the highly original horn antenna (page 182) which is to be used to experiment with communications via space satellite. When completed, the antenna will be about 50 feet long, with an aperture measuring about 20 feet by 20 feet. (The miniature model at right is in scale to the size of a man six feet tall.)

Meteorology

The United States and the Soviet Union are in a race to see whose scientists will fiist succeed in controlling weather and even climate. The head of the President's Committee on Weather Control has stated that "if an unfriendly nation gets into a position to control the large-scale weather patterns before we can, the results could be even more disastrous than nuclear warfare."

Again and again we observe that scientific developments have their constructive and destructive aspects. So it is with cloud-seeding, which can be used to increase rainfall and thus step up food production, but there are other possibilities that are sinister.

For example, cloud-seeding could conceivably be used to extend the cloud cover over hostile territory—perhaps even deprive it permanently of sunlight. Or, alternatively, seeding could serve to force open large gaps in cloud formations in order to give air raiders greatly improved visibility. Above all, the prospect that worries scientists is that a nation might discover the basic secrets of weather control and then devise methods of ruining the climate of another country.

Some future prospects

On the constructive side there are many promising possibilities. Since any black substance absorbs heat, some scientists would like to experiment with sprinkling frozen areas with lampblack or soot. The resulting absorption of solar heat would cause a thaw that might make these waste areas perfectly suitable for farming.

Another approach involves methods of increasing or decreasing rainfall. Evaporation leads eventually to rainfall, so that preventing evaporation will decrease rainfall; stimulating evaporation will increase rainfall. The United States Geological Survey is experimenting with hexadecanol, a harmless, tasteless chemical film currently used in lipstick. One of the properties of this substance is that if it is poured over water, it will seal the water in and prevent it from evaporating.

In the fairly near future it may become possible to divert hurricanes by pouring large patches of burning oil on strategic locations in the ocean. The powerful updraft from the burning oil would force the hurricane to move in a different direction. Presumably such a technique would call for an extensive warning system to keep ships and planes away from the dangerous area.

If scientists ever succeed in developing H-bombs that are free of harmful radiation, it might become possible to trim mountaintops in order to change undesirable weather conditions by redirecting wind patterns. Fanciful as this may sound, it might have some very useful applications; for example, one suggested use would be to sweep away the smog that hangs over Los Angeles.

A project that holds a perennial fascination for some scientists is the melting of the polar icecaps. There are a number of suitable techniques for accomplishing this. The explosion of H-bombs is one possible method, but unfortunately there is a catastrophic drawback—the resulting rise of sea level several hundred feet, engulfing whole coasts and wiping out such great cities as New York and London.

Tracking a hurricane

While the hurricane "Helene" was raging in September 1959 an airplane flew into the calm eye of the storm, 500 miles off Palm Beach, and dropped a metal cylinder. As the cylinder plummeted down, it released a plastic bag that opened out to form a balloon 20 feet in diameter, with a miniature radio transmitter attached.

The balloon was geared to remain suspended at a level of 6,500 feet above the ground to keep it in the eye of the hurricane. If the balloon rose above this level, an automatic adjuster released enough gas to bring the balloon back to the desired height. If the balloon sank below this altitude, another mechanism ejected enough ballast to lift it.

The transmitter, reporting shifts in the location and direction of the storm, enabled ground observers to track the hurricane's path. Later transmitters will carry more elaborate equipment capable of measuring and reporting pressure, temperature and humidity.

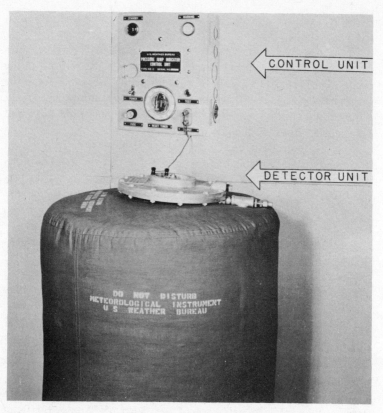

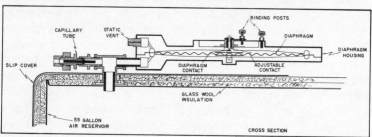

STORM DETECTOR: The Pressure Jump Indicator detects large sudden rises in atmospheric pressure that frequently indicate the coming of a tornado or other severe storm. The heart of the detecting mechanism is shown in the diagram. This instrument operates on the same principle as the rate-of-climb indicator used in aircraft.

Vanguard II

Scientists of the U.S. Weather Bureau are convinced that more precise weather prediction "could eventually save the nation's economy billions of dollars annually." The launching of the Vanguard II satellite in February 1959 was an important step in that direction. Designed to perform as a "weather eye" in outer space, this satellite was assembled to do the job of tracking cloud formations above the earth.

Once the scientists know the size and movements of the clouds, they can deduce the variations in the air masses which hold the secret of impending weather changes. They need four kinds of information about the air masses: their temperature; pressure; water content (clouds); circulation (winds).

Vanguard II supplied one kind of information—facts about the water vapor content of air masses. From this the scientists were able to infer other factors. The satellite revealed a cloud pattern which made it possible to calculate wind velocity or circulation of the air masses. Later, more complex satellites were designed to provide data on the other determining properties of air masses; when all the factors are finally put together, scientists will at last be able to predict weather on a world-wide basis.

How the satellite worked

The Vanguard II has a spherical shape. It weighs a little over 21 pounds and has a diameter of 20 inches. Although it is expected to remain in orbit for a century, it provided electronic data for only two weeks or so, until its batteries gave out.

Inside are two light-measuring reflecting telescopes for scanning the surface of the earth and spotting cloud formations. Whereas clouds reflect 80 per cent of the sunlight that falls on them, land areas reflect 20 per cent at most, while the sea reflects only 5 per cent. These differences in reflecting properties make it possible to get meaningful results from the observations.

One of the telescopes is always pointed at the earth. To get the best results, the right time for launching the satellite was carefully calculated so that it would be travelling over sunlit areas when at the perigee (lowest point) of its orbit. At this time, the telescopes can clearly take in an area of cloud formations 300 miles long and 7 miles wide.

In a period of 24 hours the satellite supplied information about clouds over about a quarter of the earth's sunlit surface. During each complete orbit of 126 minutes, scanning took place for about 50 minutes.

To record the intensity of light filtered through the telescopes, a small wafer of lead sulphide was used to produce an electrical response which varied with the strength of the light. The resulting fluctuations were transferred by a small magnetic recorder to a magnetic tape 75 feet long.

Whenever the satellite passed one of six tracking stations it received a command signal which caused it to transmit the 50 minutes of accumulated information in a speeded-up fashion that required only 50 seconds. As this data was played back it got erased from the tape, which could then be used all over again to record new information.

When the satellites reached darkened areas special instruments "sensed" the absence of light and turned off the recorder to conserve the batteries. The information received from the satellite was too complex to be analyzed directly. Instead, it had to be summarized and clarified by an electronic computer.

Making weather to order

Mark Twain's famous remark that "lots of people talk about the weather, but nobody does anything about it" has not been true for quite a few years.

In fact, Dr. Irving Langmuir, one of the outstanding American scientists of our time, once claimed that "it may prove easier to make [weather] than to predict it." While most people would dispute that statement, none would disagree about the harmful effects of bad weather.

The hurricanes of 1938 and 1944 on the eastern seaboard of the United States, for example, killed 1,150 people and caused damage amounting to almost a billion dollars. Every year tornadoes in the Midwest alone kill about 180 people, injure more than a thousand and cause destruction estimated at $70,000,000. The annual toll of

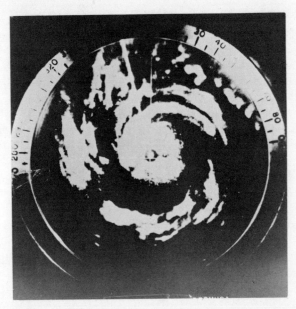

HURRICANE CENTER: A radarscope picture of the eye of a hurricane off Bermuda; altitude 10,000 feet. Radar equipment can spot storms at a distance of 150 miles (see page 43).

damage from hailstorms reaches about the same figure, while lightning results in an average of 400 forest fires every year.

The secret of predicting and controlling weather can only be unravelled by learning more about what causes it. We know that hurricanes and tornadoes start with large accumulations of rain and moisture-laden clouds. But there are great gaps in our knowledge.

Rainmaking

Drought is perhaps the most harmful of all weather conditions, as it deprives future generations as well as the present one of huge amounts of food and creates the prospect of large fertile areas turning into deserts. The challenge of artificially causing rain is therefore a very critical one.

We know that clouds are mists of tiny water droplets that float in the air until they become large enough and heavy enough to fall to the ground. To cause rain it is therefore necessary to find some way of speeding up the formation of large moisture-laden air masses.

In fairly cold weather the water droplets are massed together by ice crystals at temperatures of 40 below zero. In warmer weather the droplets are massed together by dust particles.

Man can imitate this natural process by "seeding" the clouds with such substances as dry ice, powdered salt, water spray or silver iodide. This last method is favored because it is possible to send silver iodide up into the sky by generating it from the ground.

Since the late 1940's drought has plagued some of the farming areas of the United States. Farmers have hired cloud-seeding experts in the hope of producing rain. Intensive analysis of the results showed that rainfall volume increased about 15 per cent in these areas, but the studies were not conclusive because there was no way of demonstrating rigorously that the rain might not have come down from natural causes. This proved the need for controlled experiments.

In 1957 a more convincing test took place in Santa Barbara, California, where experts seeded clouds in order to build up water reserves for hydroelectric power plants. Every day they studied the "seedability" of the clouds. On the days when the clouds were seedable, they alternated in seeding them one day and refraining the next. With conditions approximately the same, then, the experts found that rainfall was 20 per cent greater on the days when seeding took place.

In 1958 scientists from the Universities of Arizona and Chicago conducted similar experiments in Arizona. This time there was a 15 per cent increase on days when seeding occurred.

After more than 200 similar tests in Australia, Canada and South Africa, Professor B. J. Mason of London University stated that seeding clouds brings on rain "beyond all reasonable doubt." In the Australian tests, planes sprayed water into the clouds. Other successful tests gave similar results. These involved dropping small quantities of salt from planes in England, dropping salt "bombs" from balloons in East Africa, and, in Pakistan, leaving powdered salt on the ground where it was swirled aloft by winds.

A remarkable experiment of Dr. Langmuir's deserves repeating. On the same day of each week for a period of ten months in 1949-50 he seeded clouds in New Mexico with a single silver iodide generator. The rainfall records show that every Tuesday there was rain all the way from Montana to Alabama and then on the east coast a day or two later. Going back over the records of the past half-century, scientists found that the odds were 50 to 1 against such regularly recurring rainfall being due to natural causes alone.

Langmuir's astounding conclusion was that spreading a thousandth of an ounce of silver iodide through 30 cubic miles to form rain-causing ice crystals "liberates as much heat as an atomic bomb." Equally thought-provoking was his conclusion that "to get 30 per cent chance of rain per day in New Mexico, the cost of the silver iodide was only one dollar for 4,000 square miles. If similar conditions prevailed over the whole United States the cost per day to double the rainfall would be only about a couple of hundred dollars. . . . A few pounds of silver iodide would be enough for the whole U.S."

Why climate changes

Scientists have several explanations of the gradual warming-up process that is taking place on our planet. Perhaps the most popular theory is that the volume of carbon dioxide in the atmosphere determines temperature because carbon dioxide molecules have the property of absorbing and retaining infrared radiation.

Over the years more and more carbon dioxide is being released into the atmosphere through increased industrialization which leads to vastly greater consumption of fossil fuels (coal and oil). Much of this carbon comes from factory chimneys and automobile exhausts.

As the volume of carbon dioxide increases, so runs the theory, it absorbs more and more infrared radiation, with a consequent rise in temperature. Records of fuel consumption for the last hundred years indicate that man has contributed 360 billion tons of carbon dioxide to the atmosphere. This has increased the carbon dioxide content of the atmosphere by 13 per cent, which should result in raising average temperature by one degree Fahrenheit. Analysis of temperature records bears this out.

If fuel consumption continues at the present rate, about a trillion tons of carbon dioxide will have been injected into the atmosphere by the year 2000, with a rise of 3.6 degrees in average temperature. In a thousand years, still projecting the same rate of increase, the average temperature will have risen 22 degrees.

Yet there are many ways in which this alarming trend may be arrested. These include the gradual popularization of atomic fuels which do not release carbon dioxide; the possible perfecting of the fusion process; the widespread use of economical ways of producing electricity; the increased utilization of solar energy.

If the carbon-dioxide hypothesis is sound, it follows that if the supply of fossil fuels gives out—or if their consumption starts decreasing—the amount of carbon dioxide in the atmosphere would correspondingly decrease, with a consequent lowering of temperature.

Oceanography

The uncharted oceans

Although the oceans make up two-thirds of the earth's surface, they still remain largely unexplored. In fact, as a remarkable report of the National Academy of Sciences has pointed out, "we know less about many regions of the ocean today than we know about the lunar surface."

The problems that remain to be solved are of enormous scientific interest as well as of deep practical value. From the scientific point of view, as the report asserts, studies of deep-sea sediments, of the rocky formations at the bottom of the ocean, combined with further investigation of the waters and the creatures that live in them "will tell us much about the origin and evolution of the earth."

In the practical sphere, the National Academy's committee surprisingly states, "the problems to be solved concerning the oceans are at least as urgent as those of space." We need to know what controls the number of fish in various regions, the quantity of plant and animal life on which they feed, and how these quantities could be increased. "We must learn these things if we are to help solve the increasingly acute problem of providing animal protein food for the growing numbers of underfed people in the world. Considering the position of the United States in the community of nations, it seems appropriate, even essential, that we lead the way in this respect."

The military aspect is also vital. Day by day, for example, the power of submarines to launch missiles with nuclear heads becomes more efficient. But if a satisfactory international submarine control and monitoring system is ever to be negotiated, we must, the committee insists, "have the ability to make the oceans transparent so that we can track all submarines in the oceans."

Oceanographic research can also add enormously to our knowledge of climatic conditions. The committee points out:

"We know that the average weather conditions we call climate can change over a few decades, and we suspect that changes in the storage of gases and heat in the oceans will profoundly influence the process. Studies in the mechanisms of interchange between the air-sea boundaries of regions where intense interchange occurs, and of the slow mixing between the ocean deeps and the surface, which controls storage of heat and gases, are essential for further understanding, hence for prediction and possibility of control."

The world's food supply

If the present rate of population increase continues, the world's population will double to $6\frac{1}{2}$ billion by the year 2000. The only way to increase the food supply or even to maintain its present level is to extract the rich food resources of the sea. Among the possible techniques that might be used are: putting the cultivation of existing fish stocks on a scientific basis and transplanting desirable fish from one region to another. The seas could be made more productive by introducing minerals just as the farmer does. One fanciful idea that has been suggested is the use of a huge sea-stirrer that would raise phosphates and other nutrients from the bottom to the surface of the seas.

Weather prediction

The oceans act as a thermostat to keep temperatures within the limits needed to maintain human life. No less than one-third of the sun's vital energy goes into the sea. This energy leaves the oceans as moisture-bearing air, drives the world's wind currents and supplies the power for its storms. The committee of the National Academy of Sciences feels that intensive studies of the underlying conditions for ten years would make it possible to direct the winds as desired, moderate the severity of the storms and predict weather for ten years ahead.

New kinds of equipment

Oceanic research of the future will rely on novel kinds of equipment, such as the "floating laboratories" containing elaborate electronic gear, winches for dragging up extra-heavy burdens, and unusually sensitive engine controls.

Even more remarkable is the suggestion of a manned buoy

intended as a mid-ocean station. With its 30-foot diameter, such a station would have room for a crew of 30 scientists who would make observations of the sea life around them and the routes of the underwater rivers in the ocean.

The living quarters would be on the upper levels of the station, with the observation posts at mid-level. Generators, fuel, oxygen storage tanks and other equipment would be kept at the bottom, with supplies brought in by helicopter.

An ocean river

In 1959 a joint expedition of the United States Fish and Wildlife Service and the Scripps Institution of Oceanography prepared the first map of a great river, 3,500 miles long, 250 miles wide and 1,000 feet deep, that flows eastward along the Equator, ending a little east of the Galapagos Islands. The submerged current had originally been discovered six years earlier by Dr. Townsend Cromwell of the Fish and Wildlife Service.

This is considered one of the greatest discoveries in modern times in the field of oceanography. However, instead of solving any problems, it actually raises many new ones; for example, scientists realize that there must be many undiscovered currents, and they look forward to analyzing ocean structures in terms of these currents.

Exploring the earth's crust

Many years ago Jules Verne wrote a fanciful story called *Journey to the Center of the Earth*. Today one of the most remarkable and fascinating scientific projects is the so-called "Mohole" project of probing the earth's crust by digging a hole six miles deep to penetrate through the ocean floor. There are three main objectives: (1) obtaining a complete history of the earth's climate; (2) learning a great deal about the origin and evolution of life; (3) discovering decisive evidence about the origin of the earth and the moon—perhaps even of the whole solar system.

To the layman it is not apparent why the scientists should try to probe the earth's crust on the ocean bottom instead of under the land masses. The explanation is that the ocean floor has changed very little since its original formation, whereas over the last two billion years many geological layers have piled up over the crust which lies under the continental locations. Consequently, where the crust under land is anywhere from 20 to 40 miles down, the crust under the ocean bottom is only 5 to 10 miles down; in fact, there are places where it is only 3 miles below the surface.

There is still another advantage of a marine location—it is possible to exploit the techniques of offshore oil-drilling. The diggers' goal is the "Moho," the boundary between the earth's crust and its next layer.

The Moho is actually the Mohorovicic Discontinuity, so named for the Yugoslav geologist who first identified it by studying earthquake waves. Inside the Moho are three layers. The first, known as the "mantle," continues for a depth of 1,800 miles and is thought to be mainly solid. After that, scientists believe, comes the outer core, 1,400 miles deep and in a fluid or molten state. Finally there is the inner core, extending to the center of the earth. It is thought to be 800 miles deep, composed of nickel and iron.

The required drilling must take place several hundred miles away from the shore where the continental shelf (the underwater extension of the shore) ends and the ocean floor descends steeply to 2 or 3 miles. Over billions of years a sediment about 4,000 feet deep has been formed. If the scientists can get through this sediment, the theory runs, they can penetrate to the ocean floor and find it in the state that it was in when the oceans were formed and the earth and moon first took shape.

Our present knowledge of the earth's interior has all been derived from the study of earthquake waves. But if the Moho project proves practicable, scientists will be able to enormously increase their knowledge of the earth's interior.

Both the United States and the Soviet Union are in a race to see who can get to the Moho first. American scientists have several drilling sites in mind, with the one most favored off the coast of Puerto Rico.

The job may cost $15,000,000 and take four years. One of the great technical problems is the possibility that when a temperature of 600 degrees is reached during drilling, the excavated rock, having the consistency of mud, will flow right back into the drilled hole.

Mining the ocean floor

Scientists have discovered that the sea bottoms contain enormous amounts of manganese nodules that look like cannon balls. Some of them are no larger than a walnut; others are two feet in diameter. All of these nodules are rich in valuable minerals, especially manganese. Oceanographers believe that these nodules average a 20 per cent manganese content, and that there are hundreds of billions of tons of them on the ocean floor.

The United States has very little manganese ore of commercial grade, and copper, cobalt and nickel are also in short supply. All of these, however, could be obtained in sizeable quantities by means of submarine mining. Several methods have been suggested for recovering these riches. These techniques include trawler units operated by remote control to submerge, scrape off the nodules and then return to the surface. Another method would be to use bathyscaphes (specially designed underwater craft) to rake the ocean floor.

Such a bathyscaphe has a thick steel wall with Plexiglas ports. It can be comfortably occupied by two men. Attached tanks containing lithium—which is lighter than water—would provide buoyancy, and quantities of birdshot would supply the ballast needed for ascending and descending. Such a craft would be capable of descending to the bottom of the deepest point in any ocean—in fact, has been exploring the Marianas Trench in the Pacific, 7 miles deep.

Still another method of extracting the minerals would be by a huge submarine that would pump the nodules into storage chambers. The submarine, with a crew of four, would be battery powered. It would be equipped with mechanical hooks capable of grappling any desired object.

Dr. Herbert E. Hawkes and John Mero of the California Institute of Marine Researches have suggested using drag dredges, which are simple scoops that could be readily pulled along the ocean floor. An even more effective technique, they believe, would be the use of hydraulic dredges that can suck up the nodules after the fashion of a vacuum cleaner and pump them up to the surface. An underwater TV eye would scan the ocean floor for the best lodes.

Deeper and deeper

The trend in submarine construction is to make the vessels less susceptible to detection by enabling them to submerge to greater depths. A depth of 75 feet is standard, but designers are aiming for a depth of at least 1000 feet.

The added depth should enable the submarines to escape two dangers. Sonar detection is accurate for only about 800 feet; beyond that it becomes unreliable. Secondly, depth charges descend at the rate of 14 feet per second, and this is too slow to strike a fast-moving submarine. The lower the level of the submarine's course, the better its chances of escaping. Another important point is that water pressure increases with depth and correspondingly reduces the force of the explosion.

Designers are trying to develop a submarine capable of descending to the fantastic depth of 12,000 feet—more than 2 miles. Meanwhile scientists are trying to improve anti-submarine techniques. For this purpose they are using a bathyscaphe, the "Trieste," which has a 50-foot hull made of thin steel and carries 28,000 gallons of gasoline which is compressible and 30 per cent lighter than water. Underneath is a ball-shaped platform for observers.

The "Trieste" can descend 35,000 feet and possibly more. This is accomplished by admitting enough water into the float to equalize inside and outside pressures. As the water enters, it compresses the gasoline, giving the craft negative buoyancy so that it can descend.

Some of the research conclusions are proving valuable. It seems, for example, that layers of different temperatures create "tunnels" that carry sound waves for thousands of miles. In such a tunnel, the explosion of a four-pound dynamite charge near San Diego, California, can be heard near Hawaii.

Another interesting discovery is that causing a sphere to collapse under water may release more energy than an explosion against pressure. In one experiment, the spring-triggered collapse of a small hollow ball was found to produce as much force as a far larger TNT charge.

Index

Picture Credits